Dragonflies
& Damselflies

A NATURAL HISTORY

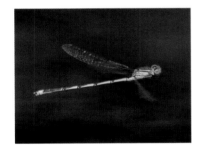

DENNIS PAULSON

IVY PRESS

First published in the UK in 2019 by
Ivy Press
An imprint of The Quarto Group
The Old Brewery, 6 Blundell Street
London N7 9BH, United Kingdom
T (0)20 7700 6700 F (0)20 7700 8066
www.QuartoKnows.com

Text © 2019 Dennis Paulson
Design and layout © 2019 Quarto Publishing plc

British Library Cataloguing-in-Publication Data
A catalogue record for this book is available from the
British Library

ISBN: 978-1-78240-563-4

This book was conceived, designed and produced by
Ivy Press
58 West Street, Brighton BN1 2RA, United Kingdom
PUBLISHER Susan Kelly
EDITORIAL DIRECTOR Tom Kitch
ART DIRECTOR James Lawrence
PROJECT EDITOR Joanna Bentley
DESIGNER James Winrow
ILLUSTRATOR John Woodcock

Printed in China
10 9 8 7 6 5 4 3 2 1

Contents

Introduction

Dragonflies and damselflies are large, colorful, active, and visible in daylight hours, so along with butterflies they have always been among the most popular insects. They are a diverse group, the order Odonata, with 6,308 described species at present, occurring on all continents but Antarctica and all islands large enough to contain fresh water. This book is about them.

There are two major groups of Odonata: dragonflies and damselflies. There is potential for confusion, as "dragonfly" in some English-speaking countries is used for both groups but in others for just one group (the "true dragonflies," suborder Anisoptera). Therefore, in this book "dragonflies" will be used when referring to the Anisoptera, "damselflies" to the other suborder, Zygoptera, and odonates when referring to all of them. It should also be noted that odonate larvae are also commonly called "nymphs" and less commonly "naiads."

Almost all odonates are tied to freshwater habitats, where their larvae live, although the adults roam far and wide. Along with butterflies, they are the largest insects seen by most of us. There are no microscopic species and many that are impressively large. They are typical insects, with six legs and two pairs of wings. They lay eggs, which hatch into larvae, which grow and molt and eventually make a final molt from the larval stage to the adult stage.

Odonates are carnivores throughout their lives. Although they are active predators, they are thought to eat no more than about 15 percent of their body weight in a day; they are certainly slim and trim. Both adults and larvae fit into the food web between the smaller insects and other arthropods that are their primary prey and the birds, many of which eat odonates. They are eaten by some species in all the other vertebrate groups (fishes, amphibians, reptiles, and mammals) as well. The web is complex, though; large larvae eat fish and tadpoles and an adult may take a hummingbird. They are also eaten by other insect predators and, of course, each other.

Other than the mosquitoes and other biting flies that they eat, dragonflies and damselflies have been of little economic significance to people. They are of great aesthetic significance, however, with their dazzling colors and aerial acrobatics enthralling anyone who stops for a moment at a wetland. This same charisma has made them favorite, almost iconic, animals of artists and designers of all sorts.

Their characteristic outline can be seen on an impressive variety of jewelry, pottery, metalware, and clothing. Dragonfly is a popular brand name, with

LEFT: Widespread in the New World tropics, *Staurophlebia reticulata* is one of the largest dragonflies in the Americas.

RIGHT: The colored wings of *Rhyothemis triangularis* make their wing movements more obvious, thus the name "flutterers" for this genus.

Dragonfly businesses in many large cities in English-speaking countries—everything from pubs to travel agencies, book stores to beauty parlors. There are novels with Dragonfly and Odonata in their titles. There is a musical group named Dragonfly, and more than 30 other musical groups have produced albums with the title Dragonfly. Damselfly clearly does not have the same cachet; that name is used only rarely.

Because odonates are such large and prominent and easily studied insects, they have also long piqued the interest of biologists, and they are of great significance to science. Their adaptations for vision, flight, display, mating, and larval life are unique and lend themselves to speculation, theorization, observation, and experimentation. The resulting research has given us invaluable insights into nature, from freshwater ecology, competition, and predation to mating strategies, metamorphosis, and migration.

One of the most interesting aspects of the Odonata, revealed again and again with close study, is the diversity of their adaptations. They very often have more than one morphological or behavioral way to accomplish a particular goal, and learning of these variations has given us an ever-growing appreciation of the special nature of these insects.

But beyond this, odonates have caught the attention of amateur naturalists everywhere. Acting as citizen scientists, these dedicated amateurs are in the field day after day documenting populations of these animals by collection, observation, and photography, and often entering their data into ever-growing online databases of greater and greater value as the record of the current status of the group.

This book embarks on a journey through the Odonata, peering into every aspect of the lives of these complex animals. In the first chapter, we learn about the evolutionary background of one of the oldest insect

This book embarks on a journey through the Odonata, peering into every aspect of the lives of these complex animals.

groups. When did they first appear? How much have they changed? What do they look like now? Where do they live? To understand their lives, we must know something about their variation in size, structure, and coloration.

But it is their behavior that is especially interesting, and the second chapter elaborates on their predatory behavior: what they eat and how they capture prey, what eats them, and how they avoid their predators. Their superb vision and unsurpassed flight abilities are what makes them both great predators and challenging prey, and those aspects of being an odonate will be emphasized throughout the book.

The third chapter delves into odonate reproductive biology. The complexity of their sex lives is notoriously interesting to biologists, as odonate reproduction contains behaviors found nowhere else in the animal kingdom. There are many dichotomies in odonate sexual behavior: elegant courtship or quick sex, copulating in flight or at rest, mating very briefly or taking inordinate time, laying eggs in or out of plants, ovipositing in flight or at rest, and other ways in which they vary a surprising amount. Odonates are above all adaptable, their facultative behavior having allowed them to survive so well into the present.

In the fourth chapter we see what goes on underwater during their extended larval life, as they are as much aquatic as they are aerial. Species breed in still or running waters, from large lakes and rivers to tiny seeps and puddles, and even containers of water well above the ground. The larvae are streamlined for fast swimming or flattened to hide among bottom detritus. They detect their prey by sight or by touch. Their emergence from the water and from their larval skin is one of the miniature spectacles of nature.

What do people have to do with odonates? That is the subject of the fifth chapter. Dragonflies have sinister reputations in some cultures and are greatly admired in others. They are wonderful organisms for research and education, and they are common in representational art, both two- and three-dimensional. Although they may be more resilient to extirpation than many other freshwater organisms, their populations are still being threatened worldwide, and strong efforts are being made and must continue to be made to preserve the wetlands that they need for life.

Finally, we would be surprised if there was not a great amount of diversity in a group with more than 6,000 species, and indeed there is. The sixth chapter explains a bit about how this diversity has come about and in addition presents the broad diversity of the group by featuring an introduction to the 39 families that make up the order Odonta.

But it is the species themselves, the endpoints of evolution, that are really the representatives of the Odonata that we all encounter. The book features profiles of 55 of them, appending the first five chapters. For each species, the family name, average total length of males, distribution, and habitat are indicated. The species accounts are often used to make points about odonate biology not covered elsewhere in the text.

After the main text, there is an extensive glossary that explains the unfamiliar terms presented about these insects, followed by lists of books and further resources, especially websites, to learn still more about them.

RIGHT: Male *Mecistogaster amalia* from Brazil, one of the longest of odonates. A long abdomen acts to stabilize slow and hovering flight for foraging around forest clearings.

CHAPTER ONE
What is a Dragonfly?

Dragonflies and damselflies have been around for at least 250 million years, appearing with the dinosaurs but long outlasting them. Insects primitive in their evolutionary history but advanced in many aspects of their biology, the two groups together are called odonates, and this is their story.

Odonate Classification and Evolution

Insects first of all

With more and more genetic studies performed in laboratories all over the world, we are getting closer to understanding the branches of the Tree of Life, from the whole animal kingdom to the phylum Arthropoda (arthropods, all with exoskeleton and jointed legs), the class Hexapoda (the insects, with only six legs), and the order Odonata (dragonflies and damselflies). Although very different in many ways from living odonates, the mayflies of the order Ephemeroptera are their closest relatives. Both are in a group of orders of aquatic insects, some of them extinct, that were the first insects to take flight.

The order Odonata first appeared in the fossil record in the Lower Permian Period, about 250 million years ago. Some early groups were distinct suborders that disappeared over time and are long extinct. But many of the families we recognize today were present by about 200 million years ago, at the beginning of the Jurassic Period and well before the dinosaurs.

Odonate wings preserve very well in the fossil record, settling to the bottom of a pond where they are slowly covered by sediments. Over millennia, these sediments harden and become the rocks that paleontologists cut open to look for those very dragonflies. Fortunately, some fossil deposits also have well-preserved bodies to be examined, for example, the Santana Formation of Brazil from the Cretaceous Period, about 100 million years ago.

Most odonatologists think the word Odonata comes from *odont*, a Greek word meaning "tooth." Perhaps this refers to the large and prominent mandibles of dragonflies, but why the "t" was lost in translation is puzzling. A letter means a lot, but nevertheless odontologists have turned up at dragonfly meetings!

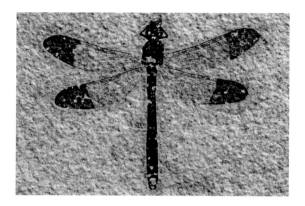

ABOVE: A well-preserved odonate fossil from a lake bed of 50 million years ago in the Eocene Green River Formation at Fossil Butte National Monument, Wyoming, USA.

The order Odonata is characterized by large eyes, tiny antennae, chewing mouthparts, a bulky thorax with well-developed wing muscles, four wings that cannot fold over the abdomen as in more advanced insects, and a long, flexible abdomen (which many think of as the "tail"). Further characteristics are found in the larva, with mouthparts including a labium specialized for prey capture and gills within the rectum or at the abdomen tip. All of these anatomical features make odonates very distinctive insects. The most similar superficially because of their long, slender abdomens and two pairs of large, clear wings are the antlions (Myrmeleontidae) and owlflies (Ascalaphidae) of the order Neuroptera, but they have longer antennae with little clubs at the end and wings that fold like those of other insects. They are also entirely terrestrial.

The suborders of Odonata

Odonates come in two easily recognizable types—dragonflies and damselflies. Dragonflies are in the suborder Anisoptera (meaning "unlike wings"). They are more robust, with large eyes either touching or closer together than their own diameter, and large, relatively broad wings with the hindwing broader than the forewing (hence "unlike wings"). The wings are always held open and perpendicular to the body axis (a very few species close them at rest). Dragonfly wings provide versatile flight over a wide range of speeds.

Damselflies are in the suborder Zygoptera (meaning "yoked wings"). They have smaller eyes separated by more than their own diameter on a somewhat rectangular head, and relatively narrow forewings and hindwings about the same shape. In most damselflies, the wings are held closed and parallel to the abdomen at rest (hence "yoked wings"). Those that hold their wings open, and there are many, can still easily be recognized by the other characteristics. Damselfly wings are adapted for controlled slow flight.

A third suborder is the Anisozygoptera, which was quite varied in the Lower Jurassic Period of the Mesozoic era, over 175 million years ago, but is represented now by only three living species in Asia. They are true relicts, not related to any other living species and greatly reduced in diversity and distribution since their heyday. They look like large damselflies at first but show dragonfly anatomy with a closer look.

ABOVE LEFT: Female *Sympetrum obtrusum* (Libellulidae) and female *Ischnura cervula* (Coenagrionidae) show the obvious differences in wings and eyes between a dragonfly and damselfly.

LEFT: An owlfly of the family Ascalaphidae. These members of the order Neuroptera are sometimes mistaken for dragonflies, but their long antennae easily distinguish them.

Insect Body Plan

Odonates make good use of the basic insect plan of a three-part body—head, thorax, and abdomen. The head with its oversize eyes turns this way and that, seeking insect prey. The thorax bears two pairs of membranous wings that launch it into the air and three pairs of spiny legs that clasp it to the perch but fold when the insect takes off and then extend forward to snare the prey in flight with formidable spines. Brought close to the mouth, the fly or beetle or butterfly is quickly dispatched by the sharp mandibles. Wings are chewed off and flutter to the ground, and the nutritious body of the insect disappears inside.

Look closely at a dragonfly and notice how slender the connection is between head and prothorax. The back of the head is concave, so from the side the "neck" can't be seen. The head can be rotated surprisingly far, at least 170° from the normal position, and tilted upward 90°. Some of these head movements may be seen by close observation.

The head itself is an especially interesting part of the dragonfly. Besides containing its minuscule brain and oversize eyes, it acts as a gravity organ, remaining stable and upright as the insect twists and turns in the air, as photos of flying dragonflies will show. Because of the slender neck, the head would seem vulnerable to any forces acting on it, as for example, when the forelegs manipulate a prey item held in the mandibles. At this time, when the wings stop beating, sclerites in the neck in a head-arrester system lock the head to the prothorax. The head is not locked when feeding on small objects in flight, so the gravity organ remains functional. Damselflies presumably have the same adaptations.

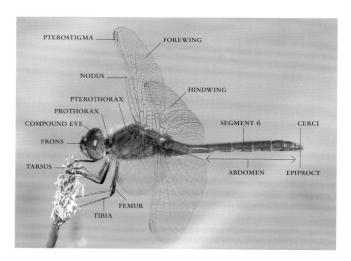

TOP: A male *Libellula luctuosa* shows the typical insect body: large eyes on the head, large wings attached to the thorax, and long abdomen extending behind.

ABOVE: The anatomy of a dragonfly.

RIGHT: Features of the head are plainly visible on *Ischnura cervula*: the huge eyes, the slender antennae, and the ocelli on top. The mandibles are hidden below.

The eyes have it

The most prominent feature of any odonate head is the pair of large, sometimes very large, eyes, touching in many groups but separated in others. Adult odonates appear to use vision as their primary distant sense. There is little evidence that they can hear, and the only sounds they make are the rustling of their wings in flight. See Chapter 2 for details of odonate vision.

Besides the eyes, there are two other organs on the head. The three ocelli form a triangle on top, with the median ocellus in front and a lateral ocellus to either side. The ocelli are not for precise vision but are sensitive to light. They are thought to detect the difference in light levels from high in the sky to below the horizon or from one side to the other, and thus are important in the quick reorientation moves made during flight. Confirmation of this comes from the discovery of a direct neural connection from the ocelli to the motor centers of the brain.

Antennae with varied functions

Antennae are used by many groups of insects for chemoreception. The antennae of a male moth are elaborate, covered with receptors for the pheromones emitted by sexually receptive females, and males can locate them at great distances. Odonates have nothing like that. Their tiny antennae are probably important in detecting air movements and thus, like the ocelli, important in regulating body orientation during flight. So much about an odonate involves adaptations for flight. Until recently there was no evidence that the adults can smell, but recent research has shown that some of the sensory pits on the antennae appear to be olfactory and stimulate neurons to fire when exposed to odors. Furthermore, in one study dragonflies in a wind tunnel were observed to collect at a point where there were fruit flies on the other side of a cotton screen.

The thorax and legs

The thorax consists of two distinct parts: a small prothorax with the first pair of legs and a much larger pterothorax with the two pairs of wings and the second and third pairs of legs. The two parts are articulated, and the prothorax acts somewhat as a part of the neck, providing some flexibility and necessary space between the large head and the large pterothorax. The pterothorax is bulky because it contains the large flight muscles. In odonates it is strongly skewed, with the ventral surface containing the legs well forward of the dorsal surface that bears the wings. This skewness reaches its maximum in damselflies, the wings of which could not be closed back along the abdomen the way they are without this anatomical shifting.

The first pair of legs are the smallest and they are not very important in perching, as in many perched dragonflies they hang out in front without contacting the substrate (not so in damselflies; the three pairs are very similar and are all involved in perching). They are, however, important in cleaning the head with the tibial comb—a section of closely packed spines toward the end of each tibia. Eye cleaning can be seen in the field by a patient observer. The prothoracic legs are also important, along with the other legs, in capturing prey.

The first pair of legs are drawn up between the head and pterothorax during perching in some groups of clubtails (Gomphidae) and skimmers (Libellulidae) and in flight in all anisopterans. The second and third pairs are folded neatly under the thorax in flight in anisopterans, presenting the least amount of drag. In damselflies, all three pairs are folded in flight but not so neatly tucked in below their relatively smaller thorax; with little space between the head and pterothorax, the first pair extends out at an angle.

A perch can be clasped by either the tarsal claws or the tibial spines on any of the six legs, and somehow the muscles working those very slender legs are able to hold the animal in place, even when its abdomen extends straight out from a stem with what looks like the most precarious contact by the legs. Only the tarsal claws are used by dragonflies perched on vertical surfaces such as tree trunks or rock faces.

TOP LEFT: Big blue eyes dominate the head of a male *Rhionaeschna multicolor*, as its six legs grasp the perch. Darners hang up to perch with the body vertical.

ABOVE: Spiracles on each side of the thorax and abdomen allow gases to pass in and out for respiration. Hairs protect the air passage from debris.

OPPOSITE: *Libellula forensis* shows the hairiness characteristic of most odonates, although not always obvious. It may be significant in holding in the heat of a warmed dragonfly.

The abdomen, respiration, and hairiness

The abdomen in dragonflies and damselflies is unusually long and slender for an insect, probably for several reasons. It is a rudder of sorts extending backward from the thorax to stabilize the insect during flight, and it has to be flexible, bending down and forward for both mating and egg-laying. The abdomen contains all the parts necessary for sexual reproduction, which is discussed in Chapter 3.

Respiration takes place through spiracles—two obvious ones on each side of the thorax and one invisible one under each of the first eight abdominal segments. A dragonfly held in the hand can easily be seen to breathe, as the abdomen expands and contracts. Watch one on a perch, and you will see the same movement. Oxygen is extracted from the air and carbon dioxide released back to it, but in insects these gases are carried by means of air tubes called tracheae. The same gases are carried by the blood in humans and other vertebrates.

Odonates look surprisingly hairy under magnification. Because a chitinous exoskeleton does not have a sense of touch like the skin of a vertebrate animal such as ourselves, they have sensory hairs or setae covering much of their body, everywhere except the surface of the eyes. A close look at any part reveals fields of these so-called sensilla, which are important as tactile organs. They can be specialized for the reception of chemical (smell), mechanical (touch), or thermal (temperature) stimuli.

Odonate Size

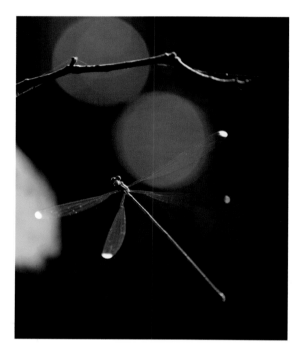

Very large insects

How do odonates compare in size with other insects? With more tha 300,000 species (55 million specimens) of insects in the collection, it would take months for a crew of 25 people at the Smithsonian Institution's National Museum of Natural History to measure a single individual of each and every species. But then we would have the numbers to show that, on average, odonates are the largest insects. Stick insects can be over twice as long, big bulky beetles and the Giant Weta (*Deinacrida* spp.) of New Zealand are 50 times heavier, and the largest moths and butterflies have a much greater wing span, but odonates are the largest insects most of us see in a day out in nature.

The largest dragonfly by sheer bulk is the Giant Petaltail (*Petalura ingentissima*) of Australian rain-forest streams. It is 4 ⁵⁄₁₆ in (11 cm) long, with a wing span of 6 ⁵⁄₁₆ in (16 cm). Most odonatologists consider the Giant Hawker (*Tetracanthagyna plagiata*) of southeastern Asia a close competitor, as are the other species of *Petalura*. The helicopter damsels, those slender damselflies of South American forests, although much lighter are greater in both dimensions. Long-tailed Helicopters (*Mecistogaster linearis*) can reach 8 ¼ in (21 cm) in length, while the largest Blue-winged Helicopters (*Megaloprepus caerulatus*) have a wingspan of just over 7 in (18 cm).

Weights of dragonflies are hard to come by. There are no weights available for *P. ingentissima* or *T. plagiata*, the bulkiest species. Common Green Darners (*Anax junius*) of both sexes average about 1.0 gram. The Dragonhunter (*Hagenius brevistylus*), one of the larger dragonflies of North America, averages about 1.1 grams, with the largest 1.26 grams. Male *Anotogaster sieboldii*, a spiketail species and the

largest odonate of Japan, average 1.6 grams but range up to 1.9 grams, and the bulkier females are surely heavier. The smallest bird, the Bee Hummingbird (*Mellisuga helenae*) of Cuba, weighs 1.6–2.0 grams, this not being much more than the very largest dragonflies. As the two North American species mentioned above have both been reported to take hummingbirds, it is fortunate for this tiny bird that the largest dragonflies are not resident in Cuba!

But there were much larger ones. Beginning about 325 million years ago and persisting for a long time in the Carboniferous Era, there were huge "dragonflies" with wingspans up to 27½ in (70 cm), so very much larger than our present-day Odonata. No whole specimens have been recovered, but they were probably at least 11¾ in (30 cm) in length. These weren't true dragonflies, however, but in a different order, the Protodonata (also called Meganisoptera), with long antennae, small eyes, and not very spiny legs. Their wings lacked some of the most important features of present-day Odonata, for example, the pterostigma

and nodus, and their larvae may have been terrestrial. Nevertheless, any dragonfly enthusiast of today would give a lot to see one, notwithstanding the risk of attack from a monstrous amphibian lurking in the same swamp.

The tiniest ones

The smallest common dragonfly is the Scarlet Dwarf (*Nannophya pygmaea*), occurring from Japan to Borneo, with a total length of ⁹⁄₁₆ in (15 mm) and wingspan of 1 in (26 mm); the exquisite *Nannophyopsis chalcosoma* is a rare species that is a bit smaller yet. At my first sighting of a *Nannophya*, I could scarcely believe that a dragonfly could be that small. The smallest damselfly, an *Agriocnemis* from Namibia, is about ¾ in (18.5 mm) long and surely weighs less than 5 milligrams, but even its petite body is large relative to so many other insects. Many species in other orders are no more than a millimeter or two in length, and there are wasps at a fraction of a millimeter, invisible to the naked eye.

Odonate Coloration

Odonates have been called "rainbows on the wing," and they do come in all colors of the rainbow. No one to date has published an analysis of any one fauna, much less all the species, to quantify the proportions colored in any particular way. If they were all unicolored, it would be easy, but many exhibit more than one color. A small number of species are entirely black or brown, without markings, but those two colors are present in most species as markings on an otherwise pale background color.

Blue is important

Interestingly, colors aren't spread at random throughout the order but seem to be characteristic of particular families or even particular genera. Blue, for example, is a very common male color in pond damsels (Coenagrionidae) and darners (Aeshnidae), where it is produced by the fine structures under the cuticle that cause only the blue part of the spectrum to be reflected (although in a way different from that in blue birds). It is much less common among the skimmers (Libellulidae), where it is almost always produced by pruinosity—a pale waxy secretion from the cuticle that also reflects the same rays. Interestingly, blue and white pruinosity reflect ultraviolet rays very strongly, so these species are vividly visible to other odonates.

Bright coloration may have evolved in male odonates simply to make them recognizable as males. In several species of damselflies in which males are blue and females are brown, painting a brown female blue causes males to reject it as a potential mate, and painting a blue male brown causes it to be quite attractive to other males.

TOP: A male *Rhyothemis plutonia* over a Malaysian pond is a spectacular skimmer, its flashing iridescent colors enhanced in flight in bright sunlight.

ABOVE: A male *Anax immaculifrons* resting over a pool in Greece combines bright sky-blue with more subtle green and pink.

OPPOSITE LEFT: Many male dragonflies and damselflies, for example this *Rhodopygia hinei* from Central America, are bright red and stand out vividly from the background.

OPPOSITE RIGHT: Two brightly colored damselflies face off in Sulawesi: *Pseudagrion crocops* (left) and *Libellago xanthocyana*.

Habitat and climate influence coloration

Species that live in the sun are often the most brightly colored. Obviously the sun reflecting off that bright color makes them very visible indeed. Species that live in darker habitats such as woodland, with much shade, usually show less bright color because of more extensive dark markings. This can be easily seen by looking at bluets (*Enallagma*) in North America and dancers (*Argia*) in the Americas. The species of sunny ponds may be almost entirely blue, those at wooded ponds and streams with much reduced blue, some mostly black; but the dark ones usually retain their distinctive blue on the thorax and abdomen tip.

The evolution of color patterns has also been influenced by the global variation in ambient temperature. With progression to higher latitude, more and more species are dark, the dark colors absorbing solar rays and the species that bear them warming up more rapidly on a cool morning. In the other direction, species of hot, dry areas tend to be paler, often covering dark markings with waxy pruinosity that reflects sunlight more effectively.

Other colors are common as well

We consider red a very conspicuous color, and there are no odonates more visible to us than the red ones. Red is scattered through odonate groups, being most prevalent in skimmers and pond damsels. The reason these two families exhibit the entire spectrum of odonate colors could be because they are very rich in species, but then there are the clubtails, the third largest family, and they are conspicuously lacking in red and blue, and are among the most cryptically colored of dragonflies.

Green is a very common camouflage color among insects, protecting them from their ever-hunting bird predators. It is surprisingly rare in male odonates, however, primarily coloring the thorax in some darners and clubtails. An almost entirely green dragonfly is a rare animal, but some pondhawks (*Erythemis*) of the Americas and the beautiful Greenbolt (*Viridithemis viridula*) of Madagascar are exceptions.

The hard exoskeleton of odonates lends itself to being shiny and metallic. Jewelwings/demoiselles (Calopterygidae) and emeralds (Corduliidae) are among the most metallic, especially some of the former, with entirely brilliant green or blue bodies. Even the wings of some of the jewelwings carry on this color scheme.

patterns of the unrelated redspots (Austropetaliidae) and funneltails (Neopetaliidae) could be a case of mimicry or perhaps a common mode of camouflage.

Jewelwings and jewels

Damselflies take colored wings to their extremes. Most species don't have a spotted pattern as is found in dragonflies, but many of them have part or all of the wing colored. Dark tips are common, and a few (the helicopters, Coenagrionidae) have white or yellow tips. Many jewelwings (Calopterygidae) have most or

LEFT: The complex pattern of a female *Pseudoleon superbus* makes Filigree Skimmer an appropriate common name. The fine banding on the eyes is quite unusual in odonates.

BELOW: *Pseudostigma* species are helicopter damsels of the American tropics. Their wings are especially broad, perhaps to enhance their agility in flight while maneuvering among the trees.

Wings of surpassing beauty

The beautiful colors of dragonflies are not limited to their bodies. Most odonate wings are transparent (in insect wings this is called hyaline), but they are patterned in many species of skimmers and quite a few damselflies in different families. Coming up with common names for these animals has been greatly facilitated by these distinctive patterns. Many anisopteran species have color at the wing bases—so many that it is cause for wonder. Do these patches of color at the bases of hindwings or both pairs of wings (but never only forewings) help to break up the outline of the thorax, confusing predators? Do they somehow function in thermoregulation, as has been speculated? Or are they just part of species-specific identification patterns?

However, many species go far beyond basal wing patches, with spots and crossbands and stripes all along the length of the wings. Some genera, for example, the pennants (*Celithemis*) of North America and flutterers (*Rhyothemis*) of the Old World, are extravagant in their wing markings, which cannot be just for thermoregulation but may well be for species recognition, as very commonly several species breed in the same habitat. The great similarity of the wing

LEFT: While perched at the side of a clear European stream, male *Calopteryx splendens* frequently open their wings in display to show the flashy wing pattern.

all of the wings iridescent, thus the name. In some the iridescence shows only on the upper side, and is thus evident only in flight—but spectacular then. Species of several families have wings that look hyaline, but their structure causes them to flash blue in flight in the sun. They can be camouflaged and then display brilliantly, a combination that is common enough in odonates to represent an important evolutionary strategy. The same adaptation has been called a "hidden badge" in birds.

The most extravagant wing coloration is in the jewel family (Chlorocyphidae), with many Asian species having brilliantly iridescent spots of a variety of colors on otherwise dark wings. The Phoenix (*Pseudolestes mirabilis*) and one genus of bannerwings (*Chalcopteryx*, Polythoridae) are similarly endowed, and the latter two show the special feature of having the forewings normal size and hyaline and the hindwings brightly colored, shorter and wider, held stationary during display while supported in the air by the fluttering forewings.

Sexual dimorphism in wings

In just a few dragonflies but a wide variety of damselflies, wing patterns are sexually dimorphic and presumably function in sex recognition and display. Odonates are among the most sexually dimorphic in coloration of insects and are comparable to birds in this way. In the great majority of species, males are more brightly colored than females. In just a few, females are brighter, and in a number of families, especially the clubtails (Gomphidae), the sexes are colored essentially the same. And there are monomorphic species within the families in which dimorphism is prevalent. But are they dimorphic for the same reasons as birds? Male birds display to other males to repel them and to females to attract them, but among the Odonata, female attraction is rare (see Chapter 3) and in many species males are not aggressive toward other males. It is quite possible that bright male colors evolved in many species so males wouldn't attempt to mate with one another.

Habitats

Odonates are creatures of the water, and the best way to see them is to visit ponds and streams and other wetlands. Their habitat choice is based on the optimal locations for egg-laying and aquatic larval development. Multiple factors influence this choice, for example, size and depth of water body, whether still or flowing, and the presence of aquatic and fringing vegetation, and sometimes (although rarely) even the species of plants. Odonates, like other aquatic insects, can detect water from a distance because of polarized ultraviolet light reflecting from a horizontal surface.

ABOVE: A male *Cordulegaster boltonii* perches by one of the small, slowly flowing clear streams that is the species' breeding habitat.

The kind of terrestrial habitats adjacent to the water also plays a part.

Still and flowing waters

Both still (lentic) and flowing (lotic) fresh water are dragonfly habitats, and every type of freshwater habitat has its species, from generalists to extreme specialists. Appropriate habitats vary from the tiniest trickles to wide, muddy rivers and from small woodland pools to vast lakes and marshes. There are more lotic than lentic species in the world, but an individual pond may support more species than a nearby stream. The frequency of stream dwellers goes up substantially in the tropics, perhaps because stream water is warmer there.

Odonate larvae are found in many different habitats and microhabitats. For example, the type of bottom substrate is very important for burrowers. In rivers and streams, some species are adapted to living in mud, others in sand, still others in gravel. In lakes and ponds, with perhaps more diverse habitats than in running water, some larvae burrow in the substrate, others sprawl in bottom detritus, and still others climb in the vegetation, using aquatic plants of all kinds. A few even walk on the bottom or swim above it briefly in open water, this in shallow wetlands where there are no fish present to capture such exposed individuals.

The importance of upland habitats

Upland habitats adjacent to the water can be very important in the lives of odonates. Neighboring woodland is essential to many species, affording shelter from rain and wind and even the midday sun that can overheat and desiccate them. They are less noticeable to their major predators, the birds, when in dense vegetation. This is especially important to the

LEFT: A typical dragonfly pond in Washington state, with an assemblage of a dozen species inhabiting its vegetation and bottom mud.

ABOVE: A rocky stream, as this one in Madagascar, will have numerous odonate species perching on the rocks and flying over the water.

tenerals—individuals that have just emerged from the water and are still not fully hardened. They have no chance of escaping from a pursuing bird, and getting into dense vegetation is their best survival strategy for their first day of life.

Forests are important to the majority of odonate species. Study after study has shown a reduction in species when forests are cleared. Fringing riparian vegetation may be sufficient for some species, while others need a greater density of trees. Some species visit the water only for breeding and spend much of their life within the forest, in many cases in the canopy.

Tropical rain forests are probably full of odonates at all levels, including right to the top of the canopy, especially during the dry season when many of them are not breeding. We have very few observations to support or refute this idea, but we often see them from canopy-access towers and walkways. While on a forest trail,

I have seen both dragonflies and damselflies foraging high overhead, many of them being too high for identification even with binoculars. It makes great sense for odonates to use the forest canopy, as there are more small insects active up there in the sunlight than down in the dense shade at the forest floor.

Phytotelmata

Odonates have colonized aquatic habitats above ground in these tropical forests. With moderate to heavy rainfall, water collects in the leaf axils of bromeliads (Bromeliaceae) in the New World and screwpines (Pandanaceae) in the Old World. Also, many trees have crevices that collect water, and these are used as larval homes by some forest odonates. Together all these above-ground "wetlands" are called phytotelmata, and more than 50 species of odonates have been recorded using them to date.

Thermoregulation and the Daily Cycle

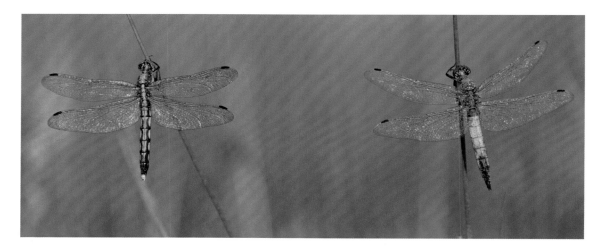

Odonates are ectotherms

Like other insects, odonates are ectotherms, their body temperature regulated by the ambient air temperature (water temperature for the larvae). They are unable to function well at lower temperatures and become dormant at the lowest temperatures, when they would be quite vulnerable to predation. Being warm is thus of great importance. They have both behavioral and physiological mechanisms to accomplish this, for example, basking in the sun early in the morning. Some species are known to roost in a spot appropriately oriented for sunrise.

Most odonates are heliophiles (sun lovers), and even in dense forests many of them seek out patches of sun falling on the forest floor. Looking for such patches is a good way to find them on a trail through tropical forest. However, even without sunlight the air is often warm enough in the tropics for insect activity, so there are species that stay in the shade (sciophiles). The most extreme of these are South American damselflies in the genus *Oxystigma*, which so far have been found active only in the rain.

Fliers generate their own heat (endothermy in this case) by the contractions of their powerful wing muscles, and they can transfer heat quite effectively from thorax to abdomen. Thus on cold mornings they warm up by whirring their wings just as bumblebees do. But because they generate heat in flight, they are also sensitive to high temperatures, and many seek the shade at midday, especially actively flying species. Species of some families, especially skimmers and clubtails, stay out in the heat but point their abdomen to the sky at midday in a position called obelisking. Still others hang downward, sometimes in the shade of a stem or leaf, to avoid full sun exposure.

TOP: Female (left) and male *Orthetrum albistylum* bask in the morning sun at a French pond. This is an example of the sexual dimorphism common among Odonata.

The day's schedule

Most odonates have a strong daily pattern of activity. Because of their dependence on air temperature to warm them, dragonflies and damselflies are late risers. Few censuses have been conducted to follow the abundance of odonates at a wetland throughout the day, but most naturalists know that there is not much point in looking for active odonates until the sun has warmed the cool night air substantially. In the temperate zone, this could be as late as 9 a.m. Even in the tropics, few species come early to the water.

Reproductive behavior is most pronounced when temperatures are highest, during midday hours, and feeding is usually before and after that. Both fliers and perchers that meet their mates at the water occasionally feed opportunistically while there, but most feeding takes place away from water. Perchers may be just as protective about their feeding territories as they are about breeding territories.

A typical day for a male would be to feed for a while in the morning, then come to the water to mate. The amount of time it stays there, either within a discrete territory or roaming, is very variable, probably correlated with the age and vigor of each male and how well fed it is, and even how many times it has already mated. This amount also varies from day to day, declining as the individual ages until perhaps it makes

ABOVE LEFT: A *Brachymesia gravida* in obelisk position, pointing its abdomen toward the Florida sun to reduce the solar rays hitting its body.

ABOVE: In the early morning spring sun, a group of *Leucorrhinia borealis* perch on a light-colored aspen trunk to warm up.

no attempt to breed in its last days. Females tend to visit the water later than males, with mating taking place in early afternoon and egg-laying later yet.

One of the least-known things about odonates is where they sleep. A site with high populations of many species during the day can be searched at night and not a single individual found. In wooded areas, some and perhaps most species fly up into the trees to sleep. Some damselflies apparently fly into dense herbaceous vegetation and then crawl even deeper into it to be sheltered from both predators and low temperatures. I have seen bluets in such a situation on a cool morning.

Ancient Greenling
Hemiphlebia mirabilis

Genetic studies as well as the distinctive anatomy of both adults and larvae have shown that this tiny Australian damselfly is the most phylogenetically isolated member of the damselflies, the sole survivor of a group that diverged from the others long ago. Furthermore, it is a very interesting species in its own right. It is a very poor flier, with the smallest wings of any odonate relative to body weight, and the odd displays of both sexes are not seen anywhere else in the order. The metallic green color of the body is found in only a few other families.

Once thought to be nearing extinction, with six known populations all apparently declining, it is now known to be in no such danger, as additional populations have been discovered since around 2010. It is in fact abundant at some locations, with densities of almost 25,000/acre (10,000/hectare) and a population estimated at more than one million individuals in each generation at Long Swamp in Discovery Bay Coastal Park, Victoria, where the most extensive biological study was done.

Very small and colored like the reed beds it inhabits, *Hemiphlebia* is easily found because both sexes engage in a "tail-flicking" behavior about every 30 seconds that calls attention to them. Both have bright white to pale blue paraprocts (inferior terminal appendages) considerably larger than those of other small damselflies, and they are prominently displayed by both sexes when they curl their abdomen upward. When a male approaches a female for mating, he lands on her wings, thereby immobilizing her. He curls his abdomen up, then brings it down, and repeats this several times, as she signals receptiveness by kinking her abdomen.

Surprisingly for such an abundant species, oviposition has still not been observed, but the structure of the ovipositor indicates that eggs are deposited in plants, as in other damselflies.

FAMILY	Hemiphlebiidae	
DISTRIBUTION	Southern Australia	
HABITAT	Riverine lagoons, ponds, and marshes (locally called swamps) that may dry out seasonally	

1 in
2.5 cm

ABOVE: Both sexes of *Hemiphlebia* have unusually large cerci, with which they advertise their presence by flicking the abdomen tip upward more than once per minute.

LEFT: Copulation in *Hemiphlebia* lasts about 10 minutes on average, most of which time is taken up by male removal of sperm from previous matings.

Beautiful Demoiselle
Calopteryx virgo

This damselfly species, named *virgo* (virgin) by Linnaeus in 1758, is the classical demoiselle, a common and wide-ranging European species and the first of its kind to be described. The species in this genus are all metallic green to blue to copper to red, and all have broad wings that vary from clear to heavily marked with black, also shining in the sun. In North America they are called jewelwings, and *Calopteryx* means "beautiful wing" in Greek ("Latin name" is an improper synonym of "scientific name," as about half of the names are Greek). When they fly, their wings are much more obvious than in species with entirely clear wings, and the flight is described as "fluttery." Because of the wing pigmentation, it is even possible to see how they move in characteristic odonate fashion, with the strokes of the hindwings offset from those of the forewings.

Demoiselles all live in cool running water. Females are courted by males displaying their beautiful wings, often right in front of the female's face. An unusual feature of the courtship is when a male lands on the water and floats downstream for a short distance, showing the female that the current is quite sufficient to provide oxygen for her eggs and larvae. The females lay eggs in submerged plants and tree rootlets that extend into the water. The larvae are slender and angular, almost sticklike, and move slowly; they probably avoid fish predation by resembling underwater rootlets.

The Ebony Jewelwing (*Calopteryx maculata*) of North America furnished the first evidence for sperm displacement in Odonata, and this discovery led to studies of many other species, most of which were found to exhibit the same behavior (see Chapter 3). Furthermore, such information in insects led to the discovery that this phenomenon occurs very widely in the animal kingdom, all the way to humans and other primates.

FAMILY	Calopterygidae
DISTRIBUTION	Widespread in western Europe, from Scandinavia and the UK east to the Ural Mountains; isolated population in Morocco
HABITAT	Forest streams with cool running water

1⅞ in
4.7 cm

RIGHT: Duller than the male, a female *Calopteryx* of any species can also be recognized by its white pterostigma and ovipositor.

Blue Barelegs
Heliocharis amazona

The name describes this large damselfly; the males are bright blue (with a green thorax in northern populations), and the legs lack spines, as well as being unusually long and slender. Leg spines in all other odonates are used to capture prey and bring it to the mouth, and yet this species and the other member of the family, Red Barelegs (*Dicterias atrosanguinea*), don't have them. They do have a long and sharp movable hook on each labial palp, better developed than in other damselflies, and this is important in holding prey. The only logical conclusion to draw from this is that they capture prey directly with their mouth, and that is exactly what a female has been seen to do—capture a small damselfly (*Protoneura*) without using its legs at all.

How this substantial deviation from odonate norm evolved is not understood, but it is possible that the very long legs are due to the larvae, which are unusually elongate and long-legged. Perhaps long legs are completely unsuited to capturing prey, and spines add unnecessary weight to a leg, so over evolutionary time this group of damselflies just lost their leg spines. The front femur is curved, which is quite unusual but apparently better for holding the long legs close against the thorax in flight.

Like so many other tropical-forest species, the biology of this one is very poorly known. Males are seen along sunlit streams in wet forest, and both sexes have been seen feeding over such streams, high enough in the canopy to find full sunlight and a supply of small insects, which they fly out to capture. But specimens can tell us a lot. No female specimen has mud on her abdomen, and the ovipositor is relatively small, so they probably oviposit in herbaceous vegetation or some other soft substrate in clean streams.

FAMILY	Dicteriadidae
DISTRIBUTION	Widespread in the Amazon Basin of South America
HABITAT	Slow-flowing sandy forest streams

$2\frac{1}{16}$ in

5.3 cm

ABOVE: The long legs of this large damselfly are clearly visible, and a closer look would show the lack of the prey-catching spines of most other odonates.

LEFT: Female damselflies are shorter than males but with a thicker abdomen to hold all their eggs. For aerodynamic reasons, the abdomens should weigh the same.

Blue Featherleg
Platycnemis pennipes

This beautiful damselfly, the European representative of its large and diverse Old World family, is known for the widened tibiae of males, used in aggressive displays against other males although not for courtship as in some other damselflies with such modified legs.

A long series of experiments performed on this species elucidated sexual recognition factors. When freshly dead individuals were presented to mature males, they would attempt to mate with immatures of either sex, as they look rather alike. Mature females were also accepted, while mature males, which show much blue, were rejected. A male would attempt to mate with a "dummy" as long as it had at least the head, thorax, and one wing. An abdomen was superfluous! If the thoracic pattern was even partly obscured, though, the potential mate was rejected, showing the importance of that pattern.

In one study, sperm translocation (see Chapter 3) happened only once out of every four copulations, and that may have signified that males in that case had copulated previously and still had sperm stored in their penis. This would be different from most studied damselflies, which translocated sperm with every mating. Specimens of a variety of species have been dissected to see what transpires internally during mating, for example, how much sperm is present in the female's sperm-storage organs after a given mating. Much more study is needed.

Females lay a single egg with each penetration of plant tissue by their sharp ovipositor, the oviposition rate varying from about 5 to 10 eggs/minute according to one study. Females are very much attracted to sites where other females are ovipositing, presumably because their presence indicates a favorable substrate and at least a temporary lack of predators. But if another individual or pair approaches too closely, females are much more likely than males to signal aggression by opening their wings widely.

FAMILY	Platycnemididae
DISTRIBUTION	Europe and far western Asia
HABITAT	Lowland streams, rivers, lakes, and ponds

1⁷⁄₁₆ in
3.6 cm

RIGHT: The expanded tibiae characteristic of *Platycnemis* are easily seen in this example in Denmark.

Common Bluetail
Ischnura elegans

Because this is one of the most common damselflies of Europe, it is one of the best studied. Long of interest because of the different color forms of females, it is only more recently that the significance of this color variety has been understood. Like other *Ischnura* species, females can be andromorphs, looking much like males, or heteromorphs, looking unlike males. Heteromorphs are more common in most populations.

There has been a long-standing debate about the evolution of this female polymorphism, and after many studies on a variety of species, questions still remain. Males seem inclined to mate with the morph that is most common in their population, and this has led to the Learned Mate Recognition hypothesis. Males kept in captivity with one morph have been found to be more likely to mate with that morph in experimental setups with both morphs present, but they switch their preference if then held first with the other morph.

Experiments in which brown females were painted blue and blue males painted brown support the idea that the bright blue color of many male damselflies is a signal that they are not available for mating. Note the significance of this in many damselfly communities with numerous species with blue males. A blue female would also not be subject to harassment by any other species.

This led to the other hypothesis of male mimicry, in which andromorphs are favored because they look more like males and are thus harassed less by males once they have already mated. Numerous studies have shown that males are less likely to approach andromorphs for mating. Also, in one study, andromorphs behaved differently from heteromorphs, spending more time in the open and being more aggressive toward males—in fact, behaving more like males.

FAMILY	Coenagrionidae
DISTRIBUTION	Temperate Eurasia from the UK to Japan
HABITAT	Most wetlands, still and running, with aquatic vegetation; even some brackish waters

1¼ in
3.2 cm

ABOVE: *Ischnura elegans* is a common pond dweller all across Europe, and studying its behavior has shown us much of interest about damselfly life.

LEFT: Females of this species have three color morphs. This one is orange when immature but becomes increasingly dull and dark with maturity.

Vagrant Emperor
Anax ephippiger

This species is a well-known migrant in Africa, traveling not only up and down that continent but also between there and southern Europe. This takes it across not one but two great barriers to freshwater organisms: the Sahara Desert and the Mediterranean Sea. Dragonflies can fly, surmounting these barriers, but few of them other than Vagrant Emperors do so on an annual basis. Its powers of flight are sufficient to have taken it to Iceland on at least three occasions, the only odonate ever recorded there, and it has apparently become established in Caribbean islands and probably the South American mainland from sufficient numbers carried across the Atlantic by easterly winds. Only documented from the New World in recent years, it may have been traveling across for a long time. It would presumably take both sexes to become established, although a fertilized female might be sufficient.

Vagrant Emperors have been reported as breeding as far north as central Europe, although it is not known if their offspring make the return trip to Africa. However, some populations in the Mediterranean region are definitely known to be resident. It is speculated that migration in *A. ephippiger* may be in part a response to overcrowding, occurring when populations in parts of northern Africa, in particular the Sahel area just south of the Sahara, reach sufficient density to stimulate this behavior.

In one study, individuals dissected in migratory flights in Uganda were all sexually immature and contained much abdominal fat. Fat is well known as the source of energy for long-distance migrant birds and, with much less known about the details, it is obvious that dragonflies use it in the same way. In museum collections, migration status can be inferred in specimens that leak grease from their stored fat onto the paper envelopes in which they are stored.

FAMILY	Aeshnidae	
DISTRIBUTION	Southern Europe, at times farther north, and throughout much of Africa and southwestern Asia	
HABITAT	Shallow ponds, often temporary, and lakes	

2½ in
6.4 cm

Dragonhunter
Hagenius brevistylus

The common name of this dragonfly species is quite appropriate, as among its varied prey there are many dragonflies, even large ones such as Common Green Darners (*Anax junius*). Among the more common dietary items are the showy jewelwing (*Calopteryx*) damselflies that live on the same streams. And like other large clubtails, it eats butterflies as well, including distasteful ones such as Monarchs (*Danaus plexippus*) and Queens (*D. gilippus*). It is one of three species of dragonflies that has been seen with a hummingbird as prey. It is likely that its very long hind legs are an adaptation to capture and hold on to such large prey. But these same legs make perching awkward for Dragonhunters, as they have to wrap them around a slender twig. With such a long abdomen, they cannot assume the obelisk position to lower their heat load at midday, so instead they perch with abdomen hanging straight down.

Most members of the clubtail family have larvae that are burrowers in sand or mud, slender, and often attenuated toward the rear to pass through the substrate smoothly. But this one has taken a quite different ecological and evolutionary pathway. The larvae live instead mixed in with bottom detritus, are broad and flat, and look as if they might be a wood chip.

Hagenius is only one of many genera—and even families—of plants and animals that show a biogeographic relationship between eastern North America and eastern Asia. Its closest relatives are the species of the genus *Sieboldius* distributed from China and Japan south to Indonesia, which are similarly large, long-legged, and voracious. And any doubt of this relationship dissipates with the almost identical larva of *Sieboldius*. We can only speculate why *Sieboldius* has evolved eight species and *Hagenius* only one.

FAMILY	Gomphidae
DISTRIBUTION	Eastern North America from southern Canada to Texas and Florida
HABITAT	Rivers, streams, and lakes

3 in
7.6 cm

LEFT: Monarch butterflies are distasteful to birds but present no threat to this female Dragonhunter, an effective predator on both other dragonflies and butterflies.

BELOW: Some dragonflies after emergence show clearly the green blood typical of insects. The larva of *Hagenius* differs greatly in shape from those of other clubtails.

Swift River Cruiser
Macromia illinoiensis

River cruisers live up to their names, flying rapidly up and down rivers and streams. At times these dragonflies approach the shore and then can be captured, which is often essential for identification. There are five rather similar-looking species in eastern North America, often several on the same river. With similar diversity in southeastern Asia, the same situation probably occurs there. This species is more confusing than some of the others, as it varies greatly with geography. Northern populations are a bit smaller and with much smaller yellow markings than those in the south; they look as different as many *Macromia* species do from one another. This is an example of a larger pattern, as several other species or species groups in other families vary in the same way in North America, with northern populations being smaller and less heavily marked.

Even with no difference in prey abundance, dragonfly larvae can become larger with the longer growing seasons of the south, perhaps adding another molt and another instar. The adults that emerge from those larvae will therefore be larger. Furthermore, with the lower temperatures of higher latitudes, it is expected that ectotherms such as dragonflies would benefit by being overall darker to absorb solar radiation on those cool mornings, thus the reduction of the yellow markings.

Members of this family are known for their long legs, an Asian species even being named *Macromia arachnomima*, "spider mimic." The long legs of the adults are a consequence of the long legs of the larvae. The broad, somewhat flattened larvae sprawl in detritus at the bottom of the stream or river and use their legs as sensory organs, extending them well outward and orienting toward any prey animal that brushes one of the legs. If the potential prey moves even closer, it is snapped up by the large labium.

FAMILY	Macromiidae
DISTRIBUTION	Eastern North America from southern Canada to Texas and Florida
HABITAT	Large streams and rivers with wooded banks

$2^{13}/_{16}$ in

7.1 cm

LEFT & ABOVE: A male Swift River Cruiser of the northern subspecies *illinoiensis* (left) is larger and less patterned than the male (top) and female of the southern *georgina*.

Southern Banded Groundling
Brachythemis leucosticta

Most odonates fly away when approached, but this one does just the opposite. Banded groundlings are among the best-known dragonflies in Africa, common everywhere from deserts to rain forests as long as there are large bodies of water with open shores. They perch on the ground, at but also well away from the water, and they are well known for accompanying large animals. As a gazelle, or these days more likely a cow, moves forward as it grazes, the dragonflies fly with it and capture small insects disturbed by it. This trait is similar to that of a common African bird, the Cattle Egret (*Bubulcus ibis*), and probably the evolution of such behavior is most likely in the landscape that Africa presents, where large grazing mammals are common.

That they also do this with humans is what has made the behavior so apparent. On one occasion as many as 50 of these dragonflies, males and females, immature and mature, accompanied a person walking at 1–2 mph (2–3 km/h). They flew 4–12 in (10–30 cm) above the ground and 3–6 ft (1–2 m) behind the person, some

individuals persisting in this behavior for 30 ft (10 m) or more. When the person stopped, some of the dragonflies also stopped and hovered and flew around him for several seconds, then departed or landed but would immediately resume the accompaniment when the person moved again.

Only in 2009 was it concluded that what was thought to be a single species is actually two sibling species, one more common in northern Africa and one in southern Africa but with a large overlap area. The Northern Banded Groundling (*Brachythemis impartita*) occurs from central Africa north to southern Europe and the Middle East. Because banded groundlings are so common, many have been preserved in collections, and they provided enough information to define the two species precisely.

FAMILY	Libellulidae
DISTRIBUTION	Throughout much of sub-Saharan Africa
HABITAT	Extensive open wetlands such as lakes, large ponds, reservoirs, and broad rivers

1¹⁄₁₄ in
3.2 cm

RIGHT: **Banded Groundlings typically perch on the ground to watch for any small insect that flies up.**

Four-spotted Skimmer
Libellula quadrimaculata

This dragonfly species is remarkable in being one of only a handful of odonates that occur around the world at northern latitudes. From Ireland to Japan and Alaska to Nova Scotia, all across the boreal forest or taiga, it is common at ponds and lakes.

Because it occurs in so many different countries, it has received many common names, usually referring to the spots at the nodus on each wing that Carolus Linnaeus saw when he named it *quadrimaculata*. Examples include Four-spotted Chaser in England, *Vierfleck* (four-spot) in Germany, and *Strekoza chetyrekhpyatnistaya* (four-spotted dragonfly) in Russia.

This brown species is rather plain to look at, which is not much good for territorial display but is better camouflage than the bright colors of its relatives when it spends time feeding in forest clearings. Even sharp-eyed birds are likely to miss a brown dragonfly perched on the ground. Some females, especially young ones, are particularly bright and handsome, however, with orange overtones in the brown and an orange wash on the wings.

The species has been studied in depth in very few parts of its range, but one dramatic difference in different parts of that range is that in Europe, populations sometimes explode in numbers, with huge swarms appearing in apparent dispersal to other regions. These migrations seem less common in recent times and have never been seen in North America nor reported from Asia, although many odonatologists and amateur naturalists are familiar with the species.

Libellula larvae have pointed eyes that project upward so they can see above the mud surface where they settle in to wait for passing prey animals. Such burrowing larvae have to have a way to draw in clean water for respiration, so the posterior end of the abdomen is also pointed and is held projecting upward.

FAMILY	Libellulidae
DISTRIBUTION	Across the entire northern hemisphere, north to the tree line and south to the central United States, southern Europe, northern India, China, and Japan
HABITAT	Lakes and ponds, usually in forested landscape

$1\,^{13}/_{16}$ in

4.5 cm

ABOVE & LEFT: Male (above) and female Four-spotted Skimmers are similar in a family known for flashy males. Conspicuousness over water has been sacrificed for camouflage away from it.

Autumn Darter
Sympetrum frequens

This species, as Akatombo, is the best-known dragonfly in Japan. It is celebrated in verse and music and in the names of restaurants and hotels. The Japanese children's song "Akatombo" is a depiction of a red dragonfly seen at sunset by an infant carried on an older sister's shoulder and in one survey was ranked as the best-loved song in Japan. There are hundreds of online videos of performers in many countries singing and playing this song on a great variety of instruments.

The dragonflies are just as interesting as their popularity should imply. The larvae emerge from lowland wetlands, commonly rice fields, in late June and early July, and the immature adults soon fly up into the mountains, some reaching as high as about 10,000 ft (a little more than 3,000 m) elevation, through much of the summer. They perch well up in the trees during this period, with no interest in mating. Their numbers in the mountains fall rapidly in August, and at this time swarms of hundreds of adults, most but not all of them fully mature, are seen in the lowlands, often in directional flights.

Breeding takes place immediately, eggs overwinter and hatch in spring, and larvae develop rapidly in early summer. This simplified life history is not fixed, as there are resident populations in the mountains of Hokkaido and some even in the lowlands of Honshu.

Sympetrum frequens has been considered an insular variant of the Spotted Darter (*S. depressiusculum*), which is widespread west to southern Europe. Morphologically intermediate specimens have been collected, which are nearly identical genetically. Assuming this is only a single species, it is surprisingly poorly known in the vast region between Japan and Europe.

FAMILY	Libellulidae
DISTRIBUTION	Japan, throughout the main islands
HABITAT	Still waters, many of them seasonal, including rice paddies and fish ponds

1⁹⁄₁₆ in

4 cm

ABOVE: The darters of
Eurasia and the meadow-
hawks of North America are
all *Sympetrum*. Few odonates
had common (English)
names until the early 2000s.

CHAPTER TWO
Capturing Prey and Avoiding Predators

Odonates are predators on other insects, and they are supremely adapted for this. With extraordinary vision and superlative flight powers, they rule the insect world. But there are other predators in the world, including birds, robber flies, and spiders taking them out of the air and fish and frogs hunting them from the water. And of course they eat each other.

Superlative Flight

Odonates are creatures of the air. They are often seen in flight, and their large wings are more obvious than those of other insects. Only butterfly wings are more conspicuous, because of their colored scales. But dragonflies are the best insect fliers, superlative in terms of high top speeds, extreme maneuverability, and the ability to hover for long periods. Their wings have been described as organs that have optimized both their mechanical structure and their biological function.

The structure of odonate wings

Odonate wings are miracles of construction, with a complex of veins that support a gossamer-thin membrane. The veins in the front are strong and rather rigid; those toward the rear are finer and more flexible. Many of the joints where veins come together are made of resilin—a protein that is elastic and allows the wings to flex and then recover. Grasshoppers have the same protein at their leg joints. Think of a slender tree trunk that bends in the wind rather than snaps. The pterostigma at the tip of each wing is a thickened cell that, because of its weight, serves to regulate pitch, adding stability to the wings as they move.

Strong wing muscles fill much of the thoracic cavity, accounting for up to 60 percent of the total weight of a dragonfly. When they contract they act on sclerites on top of the thorax to move the wings, the thorax sides acting somewhat like the fulcrum of a lever. The wings move up and down, but because they are so flexible, a wing can be "feathered" much like a propeller on an airplane, rotating around the strong veins on the front for additional versatility.

The wings are corrugated, with alternating long veins slightly higher and lower. This strengthens them

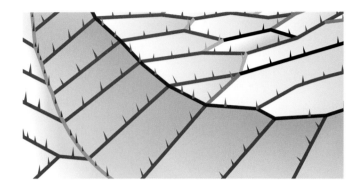

ABOVE: The veins and pleated wing surface that give the wing strength are shown in this close-up illustration.

BELOW: Odonate wings move independently, as can be seen clearly in this photo of a Blue-eyed Darner.

greatly but does not reduce their aerodynamic efficiency. They can be larger because of this strength, and larger wings allow more effective flight. Although they operate independently, the fore- and hindwings interact with one another. The hindwings suffer slightly increased drag owing to the turbulence created in front of them by the forewings, but the positive pressure generated by the hindwings actually decreases drag on the forewings.

The wings have high aspect ratios—the ratio of length to width. Long wings such as this are good for gliding but less effective for maneuverability. However, the independence of the four wings easily compensates for this constraint and allows optimal flight performance.

The wonder of odonate flight

When we apply the principles of physics to understand the flight of birds, bats, and insects, what we learn can be surprising. Much research has been carried out on odonate flight in wind tunnels. Scientists have figured out ways to attach dragonflies to devices that allow them to move their wings normally and be photographed from all angles, so every bit of their flight style can be viewed in slow motion and analyzed. It is much more difficult to learn about dragonflies in free flight, but that has also been done in controlled environments with special cameras and predetermined flight paths.

The flight of dragonflies, like that of all flying animals, comes about by a set of opposing forces: (1) *thrust* propelling them forward while countering the *drag* caused by the friction and pressure of the air, even with its low density, on the body and wings; and (2) *lift* holding them up in the air while countering *gravity*.

The two flight processes, thrust and lift, work together. Lift is provided by the wide surfaces of the wings in motion. The wings are not horizontal during flight but are inclined upward, their angle of attack greater than zero. The wings take the dragonfly upward while the opposing force of gravity keeps it on a level course. By changing the angle of attack the dragonfly can ascend or descend.

TOP: Even the bulky bodies of dragonflies such as this female Broad-bodied Chaser are easily supported by the four wings, which are very strong for their weight.

ABOVE: *Ischnura* are typical damselflies, with narrow wings and a long slender abdomen, just right for moving slowly through the vegetation to search for prey.

The abdomen itself provides flight stability, with just the right amount of weight in the "fuselage." Abdomens can be long and slender or short and broad, but they are never short and slender or long and broad. The weight of the abdomen, if not its shape, is clearly subject to aerodynamic constraints.

Forewings and hindwings work independently

Odonates can beat each of their four wings independently, which provides a maximum of aerial agility. During normal forward flight in dragonflies, the forewings and hindwings are about one-fourth out of phase in their movement. In damselflies, the wings counterstroke, one going down while the other goes up. In both cases, this is thought to reduce power requirements, because each wing travels upward in the upwash of the other, and it should favor lengthy flight periods. Gliding reduces power requirements even more, and the dragonflies that fly the longest distances have relatively broad hindwings to facilitate gliding.

Hindwings are more important than forewings in generating thrust, and they move over greater amplitude, reaching a lower position at each stroke, and thus have to beat just a little faster than the forewings. When more rapid flight is necessary, both pairs of wings move in synchrony, providing a more powerful thrust but also greater energy expenditure. The acceleration produced by such a change is evident when a dragonfly pursues prey or a male attempts to catch a female or drive another male from its territory.

By changing the orientation of the wings, odonates can hover in one spot, for example, in a territorial display between two males facing one another. Male

OPPOSITE: This *Orthetrum villosovittatum* gliding in for a landing will slow down by wing movements and then extend all its legs to grasp the perch.

ABOVE: A hovering *Aeshna palmata* shows some of the many wing positions possible when all wings work independently. Of course they also work together.

damselflies that hover over streams while waiting for females to appear can do so for long periods. It is amusing to see a hovering damselfly slowly blown backward by a breeze, but they can also add power to their strokes and remain in exactly the same spot. Dragonflies in full flight can also, as the saying goes, stop on a dime. Rapid deceleration is brought about by orienting the hindwings vertically and pushing against the air in the same way an airplane's flaps slow it down for landing.

Flight speed

Dragonflies look as if they are zipping along, but this is partly a matter of size. Cruising flight speed of moderate-sized dragonflies is about 4½ mph (2 m/s). They seem to go so much faster than that! The smaller an animal is, the faster it seems to be moving, as our visual assessment is based on something like body lengths per second rather than actual speed. Medium-sized skimmers (Libellulidae) reach 9 mph (4 m/s) in pursuit flight during territorial defense, which still seems very slow. But bear in mind that for a dragonfly that is 2 in (5 cm) long, this is 80 body lengths/second. Imagine yourself moving at that speed. The largest dragonflies, such as darners (Aeshnidae), are said to reach maximum speeds of 34 mph (15 m/s), and I can believe that when one of them eludes my attempt at capture.

Damselflies are slower, with a cruising flight speed of about 2 mph (1 m/s). They are small, and their narrow wings are not made for very rapid flight. Also, their wings become wider toward the tip, unlike those of dragonflies, and this is a less efficient wing shape. However, jewelwings (*Calopteryx*) close their wings above the abdomen at each beat, and this sort of flight has been described as clap and fling. The flinging apart of the wings on the downstroke brings a flow of air into the opening gap and creates circulation around each wing. This mechanism has been shown to be a source of lift enhancement, as much as half again as efficient as the lift produced by flapping dragonfly wings. So each suborder has its own kind of efficiency for flight.

High-quality Vision

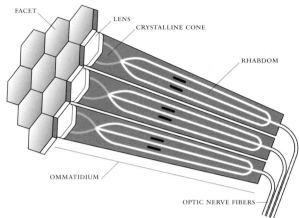

ABOVE: An insect eye consists of these ommatidia, each with a cornea, a crystalline lens behind it, a central rhabdom and optic nerves to the brain.

Dragonflies have spectacularly large eyes for their size. In larger species, each of the compound eyes contains up to 30,000 simple eyes, more than in any other insect group. The simple eyes are ommatidia, each of which functions independently of the others. When a moving object such as a smaller insect passes in front of the eyes, the neurons leading from each simple eye fire in sequence, and the brain registers a mosaic of moving images. Not only do dragonflies have the eyes to be effective aerial predators, but they have the brain as well. When going after an insect in the air, neurons in the brain predict its future location with great sensitivity, even "leading" the dragonfly in an interception trajectory as the prey passes behind an object. Amazingly, some of those neurons are connected directly to the wing muscles.

Odonate eyes are also acutely receptive to blue and ultraviolet wavelengths, so they see the sky as a very bright background against which flying insects stand out dramatically. Their large eyes allow them just about total vision in all directions. Dragonfly collectors know to swing an insect net from below and behind—the body and wings behind the eyes and the relatively poor resolution in the hindmost ommatidia making this the only blind spot. Perhaps the birds that prey on flying dragonflies also know that.

Pseudopupils

Look at a dragonfly eye and note the black pseudopupil—an area in which all of the ommatidia are pointing directly toward you and, from your angle, do not reflect any light and thus look black. The surrounding ommatidia do reflect and thus look colored. Now see how it changes in location and appearance as the eye rotates, perhaps best done with an individual in the hand. There are also secondary pseudopupils, less dark and less distinct than the most obvious one. These are caused by reflections from neighboring ommatidia. In addition, look for the band of larger ommatidia across the top of the head and extending down the sides, of different shape in different families but best developed in the darners (Aeshnidae), with their very large eyes. This dorsal acute zone looks like a "cap" on top of the eyes, often more intensely colored. This band corresponds to the most important element of vision, the direction of prey capture. The ommatidia are especially large in dusk-flying darners such as *Gynacantha* and *Triacanthagyna*, fitting them for foraging in flight in low light levels.

Color vision

Not only do odonates have enhanced motion detection, but their color vision may be the best in the world. We have trichromatic vision: three types of proteins called opsins in our eyes to register red, blue, and green light that in combination give us the color spectrum. Recent research indicates that dragonflies may have as many as 11 of these opsins, surely giving them color vision that we may not be able to imagine. No wonder they come in all the colors of the rainbow. Odonates see into the ultraviolet and detect polarized light, neither of which a mammal can do. It may be that the reason they leave the water when a cloud passes in front of the sun is not because it becomes cooler, as this happens in the tropics as well. But it is more likely that their superb vision is enhanced by some of these solar rays that we cannot even detect.

Ocelli

In addition to the compound eyes, each odonate has three simple eyes, or ocelli, arranged in a triangle on top of the head, one in the front and one on either side of the vertex. The functions of the ocelli are still poorly known, but those in dragonflies appear to be capable of detecting both form and motion, and they are important in providing visual input that affects balance and flight stability. See more under Insect Body Plan (Chapter 1).

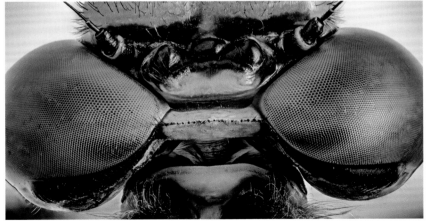

ABOVE: The large eye of a *Rhionaeschna multicolor* shows the thousands of ommatidia, the dorsal acute zone and the pseudopupils. Is it blue for vision or looks?

LEFT: *Stylurus olivaceus* shows the separated eyes of the Gomphidae, as well as ocelli and antennae. The connection between thorax and head is quite narrow.

Foraging Behavior

Three modes of foraging

Odonates forage in three distinct modes. **Hawkers** capture their flying prey while in flight themselves. This foraging method is comparable to that of swallows and swifts among the birds, and is characteristic of darners (Aeshnidae), cruisers (Macromiidae), and emeralds (Corduliidae). These large dragonflies course back and forth, often in a restricted feeding territory, while taking flying insects one by one. A flight of mosquitoes or midges is a feeding ground, sometimes for dozens of large darners. These darner swarms can contain numerous species, all feeding on the same prey. Do they find such swarms by merely encountering them, or do they seek them out in the lee of a tree grove on a windy day? Careful observations might find an answer.

Salliers are comparable to flycatchers among the birds and are characteristic of the two largest anisopteran families, clubtails (Gomphidae) and skimmers (Libellulidae). These dragonflies rest on a perch, turning their head this way and that while watching for something to fly past. These salliers dart out, grab their flying prey, and return to the same or a nearby perch to eat it.

Many damselflies, especially the larger ones, are salliers like the dragonflies. Smaller salliers like pond damsels of the genus *Argia* hold their wings slightly elevated above the abdomen, prepared for takeoff, while larger damselflies of numerous families hold the wings out as in a dragonfly, and are even quicker than other damselflies at taking off.

The skimmer family, already notable for its diversity, includes both salliers and fliers. Most are salliers, some of them with fixed feeding territories. The fliers, including such familiar species as the Wandering Glider (*Pantala flavescens*), are those without fixed

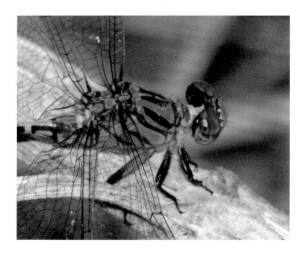

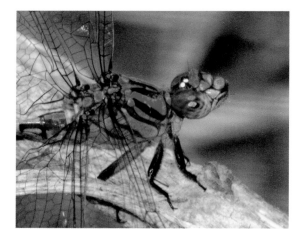

ABOVE: Two photos of *Erpetogomphus eutainia* show the range of dragonfly head movements. They can look up, down, and all around to watch for prey, predators, and mates.

territories, many of them migratory, so they are adapted to feed while on the move. Because most of them are long-distance fliers, they have relatively broad hindwings to facilitate gliding and can migrate hundreds or even thousands of miles.

Finally, there are **gleaners**, comparable to a kinglet or warbler among the birds that move slowly through the vegetation on the lookout for small stationary insects. The flying damselfly darts at one, lands, and swallow it. It is amusing to watch one repeatedly dart at a tiny dark spot on a leaf and bounce off. This is the foraging mode used by the vast majority of pond damsels (Coenagrionidae), the ones that hold their wings alongside their abdomen. Most if not all of them seem also able to follow a tiny prey insect that they have flushed out and capture it in flight. The widely separated eyes of damselflies perhaps give them better depth perception for this behavior, as they should be able to detect the exact distance to the prey insect on the motionless substrate. One wonders how well they do in a sea of grasses moving in the wind.

Spider hunting

Certain members of the Coenagrionidae specialize in spiders as prey, hunting them in their webs. The primary foraging method of helicopter damsels (*Mecistogaster*, *Megaloprepus*, and others) is to move slowly through openings in tropical forests in search of web-building spiders, then dart in to pluck them from their webs. The gleaning mode is more easily seen in these large species than in the other much smaller pond damsels in the same family. Helicopters are masters of hovering flight, stabilized in the air by their long abdomen hanging down like a rudder. Many of them have colored patches at their wingtips, and it is thought these whirling wingtips may mesmerize a spider and keep it from seeing the approaching body. One researcher noted that spiders that would retreat as a human approached would not respond in that way to one of these damselflies.

ABOVE: Damselflies such as *Coenagrion puella* rest in the vegetation, alert for flying insects, or fly slowly through it to find perched ones. Both methods succeed.

Diet and Adaptations for Predation

A carnivorous diet

There are no odonate vegetarians. They are all carnivores, adults and larvae, preying on other animals; insectivores would be a more precise term. Adaptations for predation in the adults include superlative vision and flying ability, no different from predatory birds, but odonates are also specially adapted with long, spiny legs to capture prey and bring it to the mouth where the sharp, hardened mandibles can quickly chew it up. Most adult dragonflies eat tiny insects, so small that an observer cannot tell what has been caught. Careful studies have shown aphids, leafhoppers, and small flies and moths to be the most common prey. Small flies, especially midges (Chironomidae) and mosquitoes (Culicidae), are at the top of the list, probably because they are often at high density, even in swarms.

Some species, especially large ones such as Common Green Darners (*Anax junius*), are able to take a wide range of prey sizes in flight. They eat the smaller ones on the wing but perch to handle the larger ones, even up to dragonflies their own size. A dragonfly striking another dragonfly in midair often tumbles to the ground, unable to carry it.

Damselflies take a range of prey from the tiniest of insects up to other damselflies their own size. Female damselflies are a little bulkier than males, and they need extra energy to produce clutches of eggs, so they are the sex that is most often seen with another damselfly as prey. They are especially likely to take tenerals, even of their own species, as the soft tenerals are easier to capture and easier to chew up quickly.

Large prey

Some dragonflies are specialists in large prey, for example, the Dragonhunter (*Hagenius brevistylus*) and Eastern Pondhawk (*Erythemis simplicicollis*) of North America and the Slender Skimmer (*Orthetrum sabina*) of southern Asia. These species capture and eat many butterflies and dragonflies. Even cannibalism, the eating of its own species, is well documented for

OPPOSITE LEFT: An *Ischnura ramburii* makes a meal of a teneral *Erythrodiplax minuscula* in Florida. A rapacious female damselfly can even handle a small dragonfly!

OPPOSITE RIGHT: *Pyrrhosoma nymphula* takes down a March fly, Bibionidae, in Denmark. Flies are typical of the small prey in the diets of most odonates.

LEFT: *Gomphurus dilatatus* devours *Stylurus plagiatus* in Georgia; another species of the same family only slightly different in size can make a good meal.

pondhawk. The clubtail family (Gomphidae) has many species with long hind legs abundantly provided with spines; spinylegs (*Dromogomphus*) are even named for this. The legs are the prey-capture organs, and evolution of larger spines, also seen in the pondhawk genus *Erythemis*, accompanies the predilection for large prey. Dry-sounding characters listed in identification keys such as "meso- and metafemora each with distal 3–4 spines much longer than more proximal spines" take the reader to *Erythemis*, and they are much more memorable when their functional significance is understood.

Beyond the species that routinely take other dragonflies and butterflies, three large North American dragonflies, Common Green Darner (*Anax junius*), Swamp Darner (*Epiaeschna heros*) and Dragonhunter (*Hagenius brevistylus*), have been seen to take down hummingbirds, much to the horror of watching bird lovers. Fortunately, photos taken in each instance confirm this surprising behavior.

Prey handling and digestion

Handling time can be immediate, with small prey caught one after another and shoved down the throat by the mandibles. Feeding can be very rapid: one study found that four dissected Wandering Gliders (*Pantala flavescens*) had each stuffed about 50 midges into their digestive tract. At the other extreme, a pondhawk took 20 minutes to consume a slightly smaller Blue Dasher (*Pachydiplax longipennis*). Prey items pass through the digestive tract and are thoroughly digested, leaving only residue with no nutritive value. As in other animals, this residue is defecated regularly. Odonates are sometimes seen with fresh feces hanging from the abdomen tip, not yet dislodged and a puzzle to novice odonate watchers. These tiny fecal pellets contain enough chitinous material from their insect prey that they have been used in dietary studies.

Predators and Antipredator Adaptations

Dragonflies and damselflies are actually not at the top of the wetland food web, as a great array of predators prey on them. Large bats catch many dusk-flying darners. Lizards that are sit-and-wait predators rest quietly until an insect lands near enough and then rush forward or even jump into the air to grab it. Frogs can leap amazing distances out of the water to capture a dragonfly in flight or at rest. They often miss, however, as their aim is far from perfect, having to coordinate a leap and a sticky tongue at the same time.

A bass may follow a dragonfly in flight and then jump from the water to grab it when it flies low enough. Fish, of course, are major predators on the larvae in all aquatic habitats, and they are significant enough that some species will not breed in lakes and ponds that have fish in them. This is thought to have played a part in the evolution of behavior in these species, with larvae of those living in fishless lakes more likely to spend time in the open, and those in fishy lakes in hiding.

Bird predators

Birds—75 North American species in one thorough study—are the most significant odonate predators. They are larger and faster and may be just as agile. Mature adult dragonflies are often caught by surprise when a bird approaches from below, the dragonfly's poorest angle of vision. Raptors, especially small falcons and kites, hunt them constantly. Mississippi Kites (*Ictinia mississippiensis*) time their fall migration to take advantage of the migration of Common Green Darners through Texas and eastern Mexico, where thousands of dragonflies and hundreds of kites can be seen on a good migration day in September. There is little chance of a darner high in the air escaping the larger and faster birds.

TOP: In summer and autumn, Merlins augment their normal diet of birds with high-flying aeshnids such as this *Rhionaeschna multicolor*.

ABOVE: A Pool Frog attempts capture of a *Libellula quadrimaculata* in the Netherlands by leaping into the air, a common frog behavior. They often miss.

ABOVE: The long neck and bill of a Tricolored Heron lets it snatch a *Tramea carolina* from the air as it would a fish from the water.

ABOVE RIGHT: A large robber fly *Proctacanthus rufus* has taken down an *Epiaeschna heros* with a single venomous bite.

Herons are effective dragonfly catchers, from the huge Great Blue Heron (*Ardea herodias*) to the tiny Least Bittern (*Ixobrychus exilis*). They feed by standing motionless, watching for fish below them, but when a dragonfly approaches, they pluck it out of the air. Some dragonflies may view the head or even the bill tip as a potential perch. The long, slender bills of Old World bee-eaters and New World jacamars are perfect for snapping shut across a pair of wings. Many kinds of flycatchers, including Eastern Kingbirds (*Tyrannus tyrannus*) and Great Kiskadees (*Pitangus sulphuratus*), live near the water, and the presence of an abundant supply of odonates surely influences their habitat choice. Red-winged (*Agelaius phoeniceus*) and Yellow-headed (*Xanthocephalus xanthocephalus*) Blackbirds breed in the marshes of western North America, where both species feed their young largely on emerging odonates. Several species of bluets (*Enallagma*) emerge by the hundreds or even thousands every day in spring in these very productive marshes, furnishing a never-ending supply of food. Blackbirds defend breeding territories to have access to these damselflies and structure their breeding season around the time of maximum emergence.

Arthropod predators

Spiders commonly catch adult odonates, especially tenerals that cannot fly well, in their webs. Many spiders build their webs at the waterside to take advantage of the abundance of emerging odonates. Hornets and wasps (Vespidae) and mantises (Mantidae) regularly take odonates of all sizes.

Robber flies (Asilidae) are the masters at this, even taking down dragonflies three times their size. A robber fly attacks an odonate perched or in flight and pierces its cuticle with a sharp beak full of venom. The prey becomes paralyzed almost instantly. The fly then injects the other insect with digestive enzymes and sucks out the broth produced, much in the same way that spiders treat their prey. Odonates seem to have no defense against them, and even the largest dragonflies scarcely ever pursue them, partly because they are usually perched but also because a captured robber fly could turn on its captor.

Even plants, in their own way, are predators on dragonflies. Although most kinds of carnivorous plants take small insects such as flies, some of them are large enough to trap dragonflies as well. Both pitcher plants (*Sarracenia*) and Venus Flytraps (*Dionaea muscipula*) have captured and digested odonates. Damselflies and small dragonflies are commonly caught by the sticky projections on the leaves of sundew (*Drosera*), the leaves being close enough together to trap both body and wings as the insect struggles to escape.

Predator avoidance

Odonates avoid predators in a number of ways. They usually perch out in the open, unlike many other insects, so they are relatively conspicuous to predators even when not in motion. But many of them are camouflaged, especially the females. Females spend more of their time in upland habitats away from water, where they may be subject to more kinds of predators than males of the same species flying over the water. In addition, there is no reason to be brightly colored like many of the males are. So most of them are cryptic, usually in shades of brown or tan. Repetitive thoracic and abdominal markings may increase the camouflage by breaking up the outline of the body. In numerous species of skimmers, females have dark wingtips, which may make their wings less obvious. A potential predator might be distracted by the dark wingtip spot, just as a hawk would be by the black tail tip of a white Ermine (*Mustela erminea*).

Even brightly colored males are able to reduce potential predation by changing color. At lower temperatures, when they would have difficulty flying away from a predator, males of some species (in the genera *Austrolestes*, *Argia*, and *Aeshna*) change from bright blue to dull gray. Some *Argia* males can undergo this change quickly when mating. They remain in tandem while the females oviposit, so their bright coloration would endanger both sexes.

Dull brown female damselflies are especially easily overlooked because of their small size, and they can perch under an overhanging leaf for even greater obscurity. However, they have to feed, and when doing so they become more apparent to their own predators. One way they reduce their conspicuousness is by

TOP LEFT: **A recently emerged *Erythemis collocata* is the right color to avoid scrutiny by the predatory birds that watch for dragonflies at the waterside.**

LEFT: *Tachopteryx thoreyi* rests on the trunks of large pine trees, where it is almost impossible to see until a keen-eyed dragonfly seeker spots it.

holding their wings closed, and it may be that this is exactly why most damselflies do so. The ones that hold their wings open tend to be larger species, as discussed under foraging.

Predator escape

Speed and flight agility play a part in predator avoidance, and a bird chasing a large dragonfly through the air may end in a hit or a miss as the dragonfly zigs and zags. Far too few of these chases have been captured on video to be able to analyze the details. Tenerals, with their slow and fluttery flight and less-developed flight muscles, do not stand a chance.

Predator defense

The largest dragonflies, with large, strong mandibles, might be able to fight back and escape, but this must be a rare event, as I have not seen it when I have seen them captured by birds, lizards, and frogs, as well as other odonates. What I have seen is blood seeping from a hand numerous times as someone held one of these large dragonflies too close to unprotected skin. The large and mid-sized ones can easily break the skin, especially those species that take relatively large prey and have larger mandibles accordingly. And it hurts! But bear in mind that it is easy to hold a dragonfly and keep its mandibles away from you.

Parasites

Bloodsucking flies

Like all animals, dragonflies and damselflies have many internal parasites. But their external parasites (ectoparasites) are the ones obvious to us, and they are of two types. The first are tiny flies (about the size of one to two cells in the wings) in the genus *Forcipomyia*, family Ceratopogonidae. Females of these flies feed on the hemolymph in the basal wing veins of odonates, piercing them with knifelike mouthparts, to mature their eggs just like mosquitoes take vertebrate blood to do the same. No one has determined how they find their odonate hosts. They are most common at lower latitudes, there usually being one to three individuals on a host. However, as many as seven have been found on the wings of a small damselfly and, astonishingly, 171 on a Four-spotted Skimmer (*Libellula quadrimaculata*).

Water mites

The animals much more in evidence as odonate ectoparasites are the even smaller water mites, mostly in the family Arrenuridae. Worldwide, many water mite species parasitize many species of dragonflies and damselflies. They are mostly on pond-breeding species of Lestidae, Coenagrionidae and Libellulidae, as still water is their preferred habitat. One or more mite larvae hitch a ride on an odonate larva, apparently having some way of determining that it is in its final stage, ready to emerge. When it does emerge, the mite larva, very tiny at this time, transfers quickly to the teneral.

The mite almost immediately pierces the odonate cuticle and produces a feeding tube that takes in hemolymph and digested tissue as the host matures. Probably because of where they can crawl onto the emerged odonate, mites tend to be concentrated on and under the thorax and under the abdomen. They remain on the host for up to 20 days on an individual that lives that long and may increase in volume 90-fold during that time. When the mature odonate returns to the water to breed, the mite larvae drop off. From a few observations, it appears that mites drop off only when the host is at or very near the water. Their spherical red bodies are very conspicuous, so it is easy to assess the presence of mites, and much research has been carried out on their occurrence on different species in the same environment. In general, the common water

LEFT: **A tiny Australian dragonfly *Nannophya australis* has acquired three ectoparasites, flies of the family Ceratopogonidae that will suck blood from its wing veins.**

OPPOSITE: **Parasitic water mites almost cover the thorax of a male *Lestes sponsa* in Denmark. Such heavy loads are unusual but normally cause the host little harm.**

mite species of a particular location are found on the common odonate species, so common habitat use by mite and odonate dictates host occupancy.

Following the mite is just as interesting as following the odonate. After dropping from their host, the mites transform through several stages that are free-living and predaceous on other small arthropods. They then lay the eggs that hatch into the larvae that hunt for their odonate host. The insect has been not only a food source but also the mites' mode of dispersal to a new habitat. Riding on another animal to disperse in this way is called phoresy, so these mites are both parasitic and phoretic, some of them only the latter. Mite larvae

are usually phoretic while carried by the odonate larvae, but one study found parasitic mites especially common on a dragonfly species in which they did not parasitize the flying adult.

A small mite load is unlikely to be deleterious to an odonate, but if there are enough of them, they can interfere with flight and make the host more vulnerable to predators. They can damage the teneral so it is misshapen when it hardens. Enough of them on a damselfly can impede its flight performance and make it less likely to compete successfully for mates. And they can disrupt reproduction by being attached around the male or female genitalia.

Mountain Malachite
Chlorolestes fasciatus

Males of this beautiful damselfly come in two color morphs; in some populations about 30 percent have clear wings and 70 percent have banded wings. The banding involves deposition of both melanin and pruinosity. In such cases of polymorphism, there must be an advantage in both wing types. In *Chlorolestes*, the bands are known to be associated with aggressive territoriality in males of more open habitats, but then what is the advantage of clear wings? Two of the seven species of *Chlorolestes* in South Africa have only clear-winged males, apparently thriving without the polymorphism.

Many odonates of South Africa live on streams, and studies in the Cape area have shown that at least three factors may affect their abundance and even survival. First, Rainbow Trout (*Oncorhynchus mykiss*) have been introduced into many of the streams, and both adults and larvae of malachites are susceptible to their predation. Trout are well known as predators that take insects from and even above the water surface, and malachite larvae rest exposed, perhaps having evolved in fishless environments. Second, Australian wattles (*Acacia* spp.) have been planted widely along Cape streams, and they shade out the tall grasses on which the damselflies perch and the shrubs in which they oviposit. Third, climate disruption is bringing both more droughts and more flooding, both of which have a negative effect on stream faunas.

Local threats also exist in the form of cattle trampling shore vegetation and even washing powder polluting streams where large numbers of people wash clothes, dishes, and themselves. Furthermore, this damselfly family is an old one, with relict species scattered in Australia, Asia, and Africa, as well as the Hispaniolan Malachite (*Phylolestes ethelae*) in the Caribbean. Ancient groups that are continuing to decline deserve special attempts at conservation.

FAMILY	Synlestidae
DISTRIBUTION	South Africa
HABITAT	Streams and rivers bordered by tall grasses and other overhanging vegetation

1 ¹³⁄₁₆ in
4.6 cm

ABOVE & LEFT: Banded male *Chlorolestes fasciatus* (above) are more aggressively territorial than unbanded ones (left) and live in more open habitats. They may have different mating strategies.

Variable Cora
Miocora semiopaca

Species of Odonata show variation in color, but usually within a narrow range. Pale background colors such as red, orange, yellow, blue, green, and violet can all be brighter or duller, darker or lighter. Pale markings on a mostly dark dragonfly can be more or less extensive. The same is true with dark markings on a pale dragonfly, and variability is the norm in patterned odonates such as clubtails (Gomphidae) and pond damsels (Coenagrionidae).

But this species of damselfly takes variation much further, the males being polymorphic. Polymorphism is the occurrence of more than one discrete color pattern in a species independent of sex and age. Male *M. semiopaca* occur in three very different morphs, all having the same size and structure and black abdomens. In two of them, the thorax is black in front and pale blue to yellow, heavily striped with black, on the sides.

The *semiopaca* type has extensive black wingtips, and the clear area reflects blue in the sun. The *obscura* type lacks the black wingtips and the blue reflections. The *notoxantha* type has a pale thorax, usually yellow but it can be pale blue, this possibly being an age-related change. These have long been considered separate species, but they share a very limited range and occur together wherever found. There is only one type of female, and males of all three types have been found to show interest in a female presented to them experimentally. Many odonatologists conclude they are a single species.

Although we think different male types in this species may have different behavioral strategies, that has not been determined, and it remains a good example of the confusion that can exist in taxonomy when organisms come in more than one form.

FAMILY	Polythoridae
DISTRIBUTION	Eastern Costa Rica and western Panama
HABITAT	Forest streams

1 11/16 in
4.3 cm

ABOVE: Male coras of this color flash blue as they fly over a forest stream. Differently colored males that fly with them may be the same species.

LEFT: Some males at the same streams are golden, without the black wingtips or blue flashes. If the same species, they present a very odd situation.

RIGHT: Female coras lay their eggs directly into plant tissues with a sharp-pointed and sawlike ovipositor. Each thrust pushes one or more eggs into the plant.

Fiery-eyed Dancer
Argia oenea

With 134 species in the genus, dancers of the damselfly genus *Argia* are the most diverse odonates known in the New World (*Pseudagrion* sprites with 154 species are even more diverse in the Old World). No other genus exceeds 100 species. *Argia* species are presumably so diverse because they occupy every kind of stream habitat, from tiny forest trickles to wide-open desert rivers. Most of them are habitat specialists, some even occurring on seepage areas adjacent to waterfalls. *Argia oenea* is a striking species that lives along rocky streams in relatively open country and lays its eggs into moss growing on rocks and fallen logs. Another half-dozen species share the striking red eyes and coppery thorax.

The center of *Argia* diversity is along the cordillera of mountains extending from Mexico into South America. This cordillera is interrupted by lowlands at several points, furnishing geographic and thus genetic isolation to species of different mountain ranges. Both montane and lowland species evolved by being separated on Caribbean and Pacific sides of the mountain ranges, allowing them to move in their own evolutionary trajectory. This proliferation of species in many groups of organisms has given the region the name Mesoamerican Biodiversity Hotspot.

However, the diversity in *Argia* is not entirely because of their adaptation to different stream types. Species once isolated and genetically and morphologically distinct have moved into the ranges of their sister species and added to the diversity. Some streams in Mexico and Central America feature as many as a dozen species in the genus. Further study indicates that the larvae of different species are specialized for different microhabitats, from hiding under rocks to clinging to vegetation, including mossy substrates below waterfalls. A few are even adapted to still waters and are common in ponds.

FAMILY	Coenagrionidae
DISTRIBUTION	Southwestern United States to Costa Rica
HABITAT	Wooded and open rocky streams with moderate current

1 7/16 in
3.7 cm

ABOVE: There are few insects more beautiful than these damselflies, a group of species with red eyes and coppery thorax occurring from southwestern USA to Argentina.

LEFT: Most damselflies remain in tandem during oviposition, the male holding the female to prevent any other males from mating with her and displacing his sperm.

Citrine Forktail
Ischnura hastata

This very small damselfly has superlative powers of dispersal, apparently because it is common for individuals to be taken by the wind and blown far from their origin. Indeed, in studies where nets were towed behind airplanes to capture aerial plankton at over 1000 ft (300 m) above ground, this was the only odonate collected. Not only is it the most widespread forktail species in the Americas, found on most West Indian islands, but it has also colonized the Galápagos Islands and is the only damselfly found there. Beyond that, in 1940 the species was first reported from the Azores, well out in the Atlantic Ocean and 2,600 miles (4,200 km) from the nearest source of the species in the Lesser Antilles and not even downwind from there. The origin of the population is thus speculative, perhaps introduced well in the past, but the amazing thing about it is that it is all female.

Parthenogenesis is a form of asexual reproduction. Females lay unfertilized eggs that in this species develop only into more females. This is well known in aphids and occurs in other insects such as bees, wasps, and stick insects, as well as a small number of fishes, amphibians, and reptiles, but this is the only parthenogenetic odonate. Collections made in the Azores have included only females, and 1,900 individuals that emerged from larvae collected there were all females. This reproductive strategy is quite successful in the Azores, so why hasn't it happened elsewhere or in other species?

Citrine Forktails almost surely evolved parthenogenesis after reaching the Azores, possibly long ago, but how this unique mode of reproduction within the Odonata evolved has not been determined so far. Moreover, Azores wetlands are threatened by drought, introduction of exotic fish, and cattle trampling, so conservation of this unique population should be of high priority.

FAMILY	Coenagrionidae
DISTRIBUTION	Southeastern Canada and the southwestern United States south to Colombia, Venezuela, the Guianas, and the northern Lesser Antilles; also Galápagos and the Azores
HABITAT	Open marshy ponds with emergent sedges and grasses

⅞ in
2.4 cm

ABOVE: The largely yellow abdomen that characterizes males of this tiny but wide-ranging species of dense grassy marshes is an uncommon damselfly color.

RIGHT: Females of *Ischnura hastata* are orange during the first part of their life. Males mate with them, so they are presumably sexually mature and fertile.

BELOW: Mature female Citrine Forktails develop a gray pruinosity and may be resistant to mating, as most already carry sperm to fertilize all of their eggs.

Large Red Damsel
Pyrrhosoma nymphula

This bright red species has been much studied, including studies on the larvae in the laboratory. Fortunately, odonate larvae, especially those of still waters, are quite easy to raise in captivity, and their voracious appetites make them easy to keep alive as long as they aren't placed in a situation in which cannibalism is possible. In one study where *Daphnia* (small swimming crustaceans) were given in inexhaustible numbers, final-instar larvae were found to eat up to 30 of them on the first day, with the feeding rate dropping to about 20/day thereafter. When well fed, the larvae would eat about 8 mg of *Daphnia* each day, equivalent to about one-eighth of their weight.

Even at this feeding rate, it took *P. nymphula* two years to reach emergence in the relatively short summers of northern England. The larvae reach about half size in their first summer, then grow to full size in their second one. As autumn approaches, some larvae from the year before may have developed sufficiently rapidly that they could emerge then, but there is a real advantage in synchrony to ensure that the largest number of individuals reach adulthood at the same time and are thus available to each other to mate.

As the days become shorter, the larvae are programmed to go into diapause, a physiological state that prevents further development. They build up in numbers in the final instar and overwinter in that stage, ready to emerge in large numbers in spring. The bulk of the emergence may take place over only a few days. The immatures leave the water and spend about 15 days in surrounding habitats, then return to breed. Their mature life averages only another seven days beyond that, although they can reach a maximum life span of 46 days.

FAMILY	Coenagrionidae
DISTRIBUTION	Throughout much of Europe west of the Ural Mountains, also northern Morocco
HABITAT	Well-vegetated still and running waters of all types

1⅜ in
3.5 cm

ABOVE: Large Red Damsels appear in great numbers in a burst of emergence in the spring, enhancing European ponds and streams with scarlet pins and needles.

LEFT: The male of a pair ovipositing in tandem is quite vulnerable to predation, and females have been seen with a half-eaten male projecting above them.

Common Green Darner
Anax junius

This species has the distinction of being the best-known migratory dragonfly in North America. From the evidence collected so far, much enhanced in recent years by hundreds of citizen scientists, it appears that adult *A. junius* migrate north in spring from Mexico and the southern United States. They show up at ponds in the northern US and southern Canada as early as late March, long before most dragonflies have emerged from local waters. Mating takes place soon thereafter, and the eggs hatch quickly into larvae that with their voracious appetite grow rapidly in the warm water and undergo eclosion by August. The newly emerged adults gather, sometimes in immense numbers—millions have been estimated in some flights—and head south. These migratory assemblages are best known along the shores of the Great Lakes, the Atlantic coast at Cape May, the Gulf coast from Texas to Florida, and the coastal plain of Veracruz in Mexico.

Some darners are seen in tandem pairs during this migration and apparently stop to breed along the way. Most continue until they reach low latitudes, flying over ponds in California, Veracruz, and Florida alike in the autumn. Mating pairs are everywhere at such times. Many of the ponds frequented by the darners are seasonal and thus lack fish, so the dragonflies are at the top of the food chain in these ponds. The offspring of these migrants presumably develop through the winter, emerge in early spring, and migrate north, completing the cycle. This migration with two separate generations undergoing it is quite different from that in birds with their back-and-forth migration every year and also different from Monarchs (*Danaus plexippus*), in which the individuals that migrate south return north after spending the winter in Mexico. Other insects, for example, Migratory Locusts (*Locusta migratoria*), also combine multiple generations with a migratory lifestyle.

FAMILY	Aeshnidae
DISTRIBUTION	Throughout North America from southern Canada to central Mexico and the western Caribbean, also Hawaii; has dispersed to western Europe and eastern Asia
HABITAT	Open ponds and lakes, both permanent and temporary

3 in
7.6 cm

LEFT & ABOVE: Most dragonflies are sexually dimorphic, and *Anax junius* shows this well, with the abdomen blue in males (above) and violet to brown in females.

BELOW: A female dragonfly laying eggs in the open would be subject to harassment, avoided by the male accompanying his mate through the process of oviposition.

Common Tiger
Ictinogomphus ferox

Males of this species are territorial but spend long periods perching. With very short legs for a large dragonfly, they rarely rest on a flat substrate like many other members of the family do but are usually perched on small twigs.

When studied at Lake Victoria, they were found to need a thoracic temperature of 91–95°F (33–35°C) for strong flight. As the air temperature rarely reached that level, the dragonflies warmed up by frequent wing-whirring and orientation of the abdomen to take the greatest advantage of solar radiation. Males perched high on shrubs at mid-morning, then moved lower and lower as the air heated up and winds picked up. Very sensitive to temperature, they flew away from the water after only a few minutes of the sun being obscured by clouds, then returned when the sun reappeared. Odonates as a group seem very attuned to sunlight, perhaps for both thermoregulatory and visual reasons. They are quicker in their behavior when warmer, and they can fly faster and see better.

Common Tigers are generalist predators, as is the case with almost all odonates. Among other species at Lake Victoria, they fed on stink bugs that possessed powerful chemicals to deter predation, but it was clear that the predators to be deterred were vertebrates such as birds and lizards. Apparently no insect that we consider toxic and distasteful is rejected as prey by an odonate.

When an individual of this species emerges, the adult is very green, from the color of its blood. Over a few days, the blood becomes nearly colorless. It has been suggested that a diet of certain midge larvae (Chironomidae) may cause this. These midges also have green blood, the color coming from biliverdin produced due to the breakdown of hemoglobin. Very few odonate larvae have green blood, so its presence may be indicative of a particular diet.

FAMILY	Gomphidae
DISTRIBUTION	Widespread in sub-Saharan Africa
HABITAT	Large water bodies, both still and flowing, bordered by tall emergent vegetation

3¹⁄₁₆ in
7.8 cm

RIGHT: *Ictinogomphus* shows well the expanded abdominal segments that give the family Gomphidae the name "clubtails."

Madagascar Cruiser
Phyllomacromia trifasciata

One of the many interesting aspects of odonate coloration is the similarities of color patterns among unrelated species that live in the same habitat. This may represent similar adaptations for the same life style and/or habitat. But there are other possibilities, including mimicry. So far, no odonate species has been thought to be a mimic of another, but there is much we don't know. There are a few small species that are thought to mimic wasps and gain some protection from potential predators in that way.

But what about these species from Madagascar? *Phyllomacromia* is an African genus of dragonflies with 36 species, and most of them look quite similar. However, none of the others have the color pattern of *P. trifasciata* in Madagascar. The genus *Nesocordulia* is confined to Madagascar and the nearby Comoros, with six species. Two of them, including *N. malgassica* shown here, have color patterns very similar to that of the Madagascar *Phyllomacromia*. Finally, the very large genus *Onychogomphus* of Europe, Africa, and Asia contains 44 species, and it appears that the only one with such a similar color pattern is *O. aequistylus* of Madagascar, although other species in Asia have some reddish coloration there. Furthermore, Madagascar has species of the gomphid genera *Isomma* and *Paragomphus* with similar color patterns.

The three species illustrated, each in a different family, are widespread and fairly common in Madagascar. The first two are fliers, foraging and seeking mates in flight, while the *Onychogomphus* species, a member of the clubtail family Gomphidae, is a percher. All of them flying over a stream would look somewhat similar, but whether this is a coincidence or something much more interesting biologically is unknown. What could be the significance of being a vivid black-and-yellow banded dragonfly with a red-tipped abdomen flying around with unrelated species that look the same?

FAMILY	Macromiidae
DISTRIBUTION	Madagascar
HABITAT	Streams and rivers with wooded banks

$2^{13}/_{16}$ in
7.1 cm

Capturing Prey and Avoiding Predators

LEFT: *Phyllomacromia trifasciata* is a cruiser endemic to Madagascar, where it flies up and down streams looking for females and then hangs up in woodland trees.

BELOW LEFT: *Nesocordulia malgassica* flies on some of the same streams as the distantly related *Phyllomacromia*, and, although smaller, has a surprisingly similar color pattern.

BELOW: Although in the unrelated family Gomphidae and a percher rather than a hanger, *Onychogomphus aequistylus* of the same streams is again very similarly colored.

Oriental Scarlet
Crocothemis servilia

This species is one of the most ubiquitous dragonflies in southern Asia. It is called Scarlet Skimmer in the Americas, where it is introduced—the only introduced odonate established on any continent. We have no idea where the American populations were first established, in the Greater Antilles or Florida, but presumably the species spread naturally from its point of introduction. A very successful species on its home ground can often be a dramatically successful immigrant when introduced into similar environments. Fortunately, in the case of this species, there is no evidence that it is displacing or otherwise harming any native species. So far, odonates are lacking from any list of invasive species.

Although probably introduced inadvertently, perhaps as larvae in a shipment of aquatic plants, the beauty of the males might even lead to a purposeful introduction by anyone who valued red dragonflies, as they do in Japan, for example. At close range the narrow blue-gray strip at the rear of each eye in males adds accent to the fire-engine red of the rest of the animal. Red is conspicuous against both green vegetation and blue sky and water, perhaps explaining its prevalence in male odonates.

The Oriental Scarlet looks almost identical to its near relative that occurs throughout Africa and east into the Himalayas, the equally ubiquitous Broad Scarlet (*Crocothemis erythraea*). In the region of overlap, the narrow black line down the abdomen separates it from the latter species.

The Broad Scarlet is now a poster child for the changes occurring in distribution in odonates because of global climate change. Previously known from far southern Europe, it has invaded central European countries one by one and now occurs north to Germany and Belarus, becoming yet more common in these countries year after year. It has turned up in the British Isles repeatedly without so far becoming resident. The same phenomenon, of southern Odonata moving northward, is being documented all across the northern hemisphere.

FAMILY	Libellulidae
DISTRIBUTION	Widespread in tropical and subtropical Asia, from the Middle East to Japan and south through the Greater and Lesser Sunda Islands, the Philippines, and Sulawesi; also successful where introduced to Cuba, Jamaica, Puerto Rico, Florida, and Hawaii
HABITAT	Any kind of open wetland, including artificial ponds and rice paddies

1⅝ in
4.1 cm

ABOVE: The red coloration of males of many skimmers, strikingly obvious in the Oriental Scarlet, makes them conspicuous against most of the background colors in nature.

FAR LEFT: Female scarlets are much duller than males, illustrating camouflage rather than display. The extended subgenital plate at the abdomen tip can hold a cluster of eggs.

LEFT: In Africa and southern Europe, the Oriental Scarlet is replaced by the very similar Broad Scarlet. Both are among the most successful tropical dragonflies.

Scarlet Dwarf
Nannophya pygmaea

This is the most abundant and widespread species of this genus of tiny dragonflies, smaller than almost all damselflies. Males are very active, defending territories as small as 10¾ square ft (1 m²), and have been described in the literature as "extremely active sexually." Males can be territorial or not, but females that mate with territorial males have higher reproductive success, as these males occupy sites with higher egg hatchability. Although not bright like the males, females are strikingly patterned and are thought to be effective mimics of wasps, which is something only a small dragonfly can do. The abdomen is even pinched into somewhat of a wasp waist.

The combination of very small size and very wide distribution, including on many islands, raises the question of how such an insect can disperse so well. Large, strong-flying dragonflies have no difficulty moving long distances over both land and water, and some damselflies are known to fly up and up and drift with the wind. But how does a tiny dragonfly do it? It is difficult to conceive of a *Nannophya* lifting up from the sedges and ascending skyward.

Nevertheless, it is equally difficult to conceive of one flying across a 50-mile (80-km) channel from one island to the next. It was no more than 20,000 years ago that the Greater Sunda Islands (including Borneo, Sumatra, and Java) were connected by land bridge, and this species could easily have spread through that entire region. However, New Guinea and the islands around it were always separated from the more westerly islands by open sea. So land bridges at times of lowered sea levels explain some of the distribution of a species such as this but not all, and we are left with the same puzzle.

FAMILY	Libellulidae
DISTRIBUTION	Eastern Asia, from China and Japan to the islands of the Greater Sunda Islands and New Guinea
HABITAT	Wide diversity of habitats, from grassy lake margins to tiny acid sedge-bordered streams, in open or forest clearings

¹¹⁄₁₆ in
1.7 cm

ABOVE: It is hard to imagine a dragonfly smaller than *Nannophya pygmaea*, but it makes up for its size in bright color and high activity levels.

LEFT: Female Scarlet Dwarfs are so different from the males that they could be a different species. Small size and banded abdomen makes them effective wasp mimics.

Black Saddlebags
Tramea lacerata

Species of the genus *Tramea* resemble the gliders of the genus *Pantala*, all being robust dragonflies with broad wings and strong flight. The larvae live in somewhat the same habitats and are also very similar-looking, yet genetic analysis indicates that the two genera are not closely related—seemingly a good example of convergent evolution in both adults and larvae within a dragonfly family. Over the course of evolution, animals with similar lifestyles may end up looking alike, no matter how different their ancestors.

A number of *Tramea* species, including this one, are at least partly migratory, adults appearing in spring farther north than their larvae can develop over the winter. They lay eggs, and the warm waters of summer allow the larvae to grow up rapidly and emerge in a few months, at least some of those adults dispersing to breed somewhere to the south.

Saddlebags have an unusual style of oviposition, shared only with the related genus *Hydrobasileus* among all dragonflies. A pair in tandem will fly around and around low over an open wetland, then suddenly stop in midair; the male releases the female, she drops to the water and lays a cluster of eggs, then she rises and he captures her again. This is very quick. The long, simple cerci of males are surely an adaptation to this, and in this characteristic, they differ greatly from *Pantala*.

Congeneric Keyhole Gliders (*Tramea basilaris*) are distributed widely across sub-Saharan Africa. They are also highly dispersive, and apparently they get picked up by the trade winds at times and carried across the tropical Atlantic, where they have turned up in Cuba, Guadeloupe, Martinique, and Suriname, even numerous breeding individuals on one occasion. However, none of these populations persisted as far as is known.

FAMILY	Libellulidae
DISTRIBUTION	North America, from southern Canada to northern Mexico
HABITAT	Open ponds and lakes; can be seen anywhere moving through open country

2¹⁄₁₆ in
5.3 cm

RIGHT: Its tattered wings indicate that this Black Saddlebags has been around for a while, though it may live for several months.

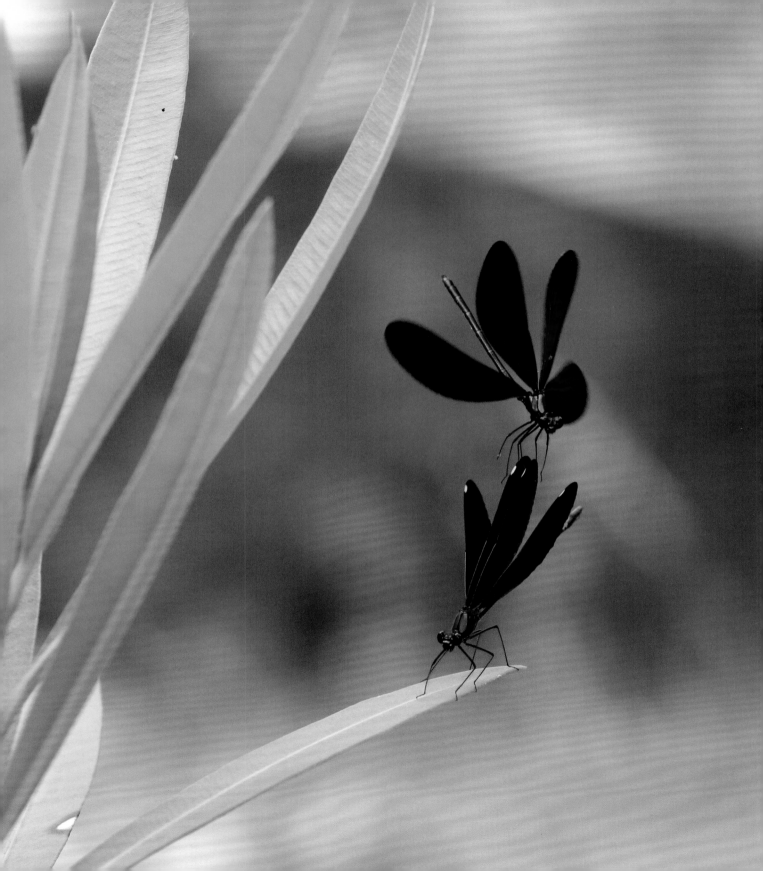

CHAPTER THREE
Reproduction

The reproductive tactics of odonates are unique, with two points of contact during copulation, unusual behaviors such as sperm translocation and sperm displacement, and even two quite different ways of depositing their eggs. Mating is intense, and fertilized females have had to evolve multiple ways of avoiding persistent males.

The Mating Game

The rendezvous

Although not so ephemeral as the adult mayflies, some of which are notorious for living less than a day, adult odonates do not have long lives, and they must allocate them to feeding, basking, and reproducing. The overriding goal of an adult odonate is to mate, and by eating enough, avoiding being eaten, and living as long as possible, it is more likely to fulfill that goal.

Thus as soon as they mature sexually, they spend a great deal of time mating or attempting to mate. In most species, males and females meet at the water to mate. This is where the female must lay her eggs, so it is efficient for them to come to what has been called the *rendezvous*. But there are exceptions to this. Males also hunt for females in areas near their aquatic habitats in some species, and in others this is their only strategy. Competition for a mate will always be less away from the dense male populations at the water, so it could be best to be well away from the waterside, where a copulating pair would be safe from harassment by other males.

Surprisingly, even breeding odonates don't necessarily visit the water every day. In some well-studied species, with many individuals distinctively marked and easily noted by researchers, a given male might visit only every other day and a female even less often. Mating activities involve a great expenditure of energy, and odonates may need time out for intense feeding bouts to allow replenishment of sperm and eggs and even body condition, as males in better condition often win territorial disputes. One study found that a male Blue Dasher (*Pachydiplax longipennis*) needed to feed for more than three hours to meet its daily energy requirements, and environmental conditions, especially adverse weather, may make that impossible on some days.

TOP: Male *Calophlebia karschi* in Madagascar perch conspicuously in the open and defend a breeding territory from other males of their own species.

ABOVE: By his behavior, a male *Calopteryx virgo* is trying to convince the perched female to mate with him. He may or may not be successful.

LEFT: These male *Rhinocypha perforata* are interacting in display flight over their home stream in Malaysia, each trying to obtain or keep a mating territory.

Territoriality

Many dragonflies are highly territorial, defending an area with appropriate oviposition sites and checking out every dragonfly of more or less appropriate size and color that enters the territory. A male is less likely to have a chance to mate with an approaching female if another male is present nearby, thus the evolution of territorial behavior that increases the spacing between individuals. By maintaining a fixed territory, a male much improves his chance of mating, as females are a limited resource, there being one female to every ten or even every hundred males at the water at any one time. Thus competition for females is fierce and drives much of the behavior of both sexes.

Territories tend to vary with the size of the species, as expected. A larger male can watch and patrol a larger area, and the larger the area, the more females are likely to visit it. Males often display at one another as part of their interaction, and the bright abdomens of many species of skimmers (Libellulidae) are important in

this display. In some species, males raise their abdomen while facing each other and hovering. In others they fly in parallel and display their broad, brightly colored abdomens. Most physical clashes rarely seem to do much damage but have the effect of getting rid of an intruder. Nevertheless, aggression can be fierce enough that males grapple and bite one another, sometimes causing disabling injuries.

Some territorial disputes are "wars of attrition." Males of some jewelwing (*Calopteryx*) damselflies circle around and around one another, moving over a disputed territory for minutes at a time, until one of them leaves the water. The one remaining is usually the one with greater fat reserves, having fed more effectively. It can take some time (occasionally up to several hours) for the loser to acknowledge defeat. Other factors involved in territory holding include size, age, flight agility, and incumbency (residence on the territory).

Territory sizes can be surprisingly large. A large darner (*Aeshna*), constantly in flight, may attempt to

defend a territory of up to around 20,000 ft² (1,800 m²), and he may or may not come upon an ovipositing female for all of those efforts. A male spiketail (*Cordulegaster*) may fly up a stream for 1,000 ft (300 m) in patrol, then turn and fly back down, fiercely chasing away any other male encountered. This increases the opportunity to intercept one of the few females that will visit the stream on a given day.

Nonterritorial species
Many species, especially "fliers" (Aeshnidae and others), just fly along a shoreline in search of females. Female darners spend most of their time at rest, as they are laying eggs, and males are more likely to encounter a female if they range over a large area. They do not defend fixed territories, but they do chase each other at every encounter. It may be that many male chases are cases of mistaken identity, a male approaching any other individual that he detects in a mating attempt, then at close range detecting that it is not a conspecific female. At the water, it is much more likely to be

another male, hence the often frantic activity of males holding territories.

The majority of male damselflies, especially the smaller ones, are not territorial; simply, they attempt mating with any female they encounter. At times there may be virtual swarms of hundreds of these nonterritorial individuals flying over the water or perching on sedge stems. Even very small species of both dragonflies and damselflies, however, may defend very small territories. Interestingly, several studies have shown that males alternating territorial and nonterritorial behavior have the highest mating success.

Courtship
Courtship is widely varied through damselfly families, sometimes being as elaborate as anything done by a bird. River Jewelwing (*Calopteryx aequabilis*) males flutter in front of females, their black-tipped wings outlining their flashy emerald body. They then land on the water and float past, presumably informing the female that the current speed is appropriate—fast

OPPOSITE: *Calopteryx virgo* is typical of the demoiselles in its broad wings and spectacular displays, male to male for territory and male to female for mating.

LEFT: Pond damselflies such as these *Enallagma clausum* bluets do not defend territories, but males come to the water to compete for females that appear.

enough for good oxygenation, slow enough that eggs won't be washed away—and thus conditions are just right for mating. Damselflies of several families have spectacular flight displays, some described in the species accounts in this book. In Africa, chlorocyphids display with their expanded tibiae. Species in both China (*Pseudolestes mirabilis*) and South America (*Chalcopteryx* spp.) have hyaline forewings and colored hindwings. A male will fly with only the forewings and thus display the stationary hindwings to a female.

Some dragonflies practice courtship, this apparently being limited to species that maintain territories.

Not only does the male exclude rival males from his territory, but he must still convince a female that enters the territory to mate with him. Most of the courtship behavior that has been observed has been in the family Libellulidae, many of the species having strong sexual dimorphism and brightly colored males. A male will vigorously defend a territory around a likely oviposition site, which is usually a plant or cluster of plants. When he sees a female, he flies toward her and then reverses, slowly flying back to his special site. If she is interested in mating, she will follow. He then either lands or hovers nearby, and as she approaches, he takes her in tandem.

Mating

Dragonfly mating

Male dragonflies may capture their prospective mate in flight or at rest. To take a female in tandem, the male grabs her by the thorax, quickly curling his abdomen forward to get a firm hold on the female's head with his terminal appendages. Dragonflies have three of these appendages—an inferior one (epiproct) that fits on the top of the female's head and two superior ones (cerci, singular cercus) that lie along the back of the head on either side of the neck, in a viselike grip that she can't break. In fact, the grip is so tight that punctures are often left on the female's eyes and even in the chitin of the head itself from sharp corners and spines on male epiprocts and cerci. The female then swings the end of her abdomen up and connects to the male's abdomen at his second abdominal segment. This is called the wheel position.

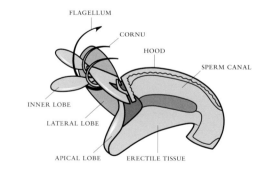

FLAGELLUM

CORNU

HOOD

SPERM CANAL

INNER LOBE

LATERAL LOBE

APICAL LOBE

ERECTILE TISSUE

The sperm, as in all other animals, are produced in the testes—linear organs that lie on either side of the digestive tract and deliver their contents through the genital opening (gonopore) on segment 9 of the 10-segmented abdomen. Either well before or just before copulation, all male anisopterans transfer sperm from the gonopore to the penis, or vesica spermalis, which originates on segment 3. This is called sperm translocation. This separation of the copulatory organ from the genital opening is unique to Odonata. There are hypotheses attempting to explain how this might have evolved through an intermediate stage of males depositing their sperm on the ground, as do some wingless insects, and females picking it up from there.

Damselfly mating

Damselfly mating is much the same except for the point of connection. Just as in dragonflies, a male damselfly lands on the thorax of a female, but in this case he connects with the anterior part of her thorax. His inferior appendages (paraprocts) rest on or grasp her prothorax, and his superior appendages (cerci) lock into narrow plates on the front of the pterothorax or, if long and forcepslike, clasp the junction between the prothorax and pterothorax. With their long, slender abdomens, the wheel position in damselflies looks like a heart—an appropriate symbol for Valentine's Day.

The penis of damselflies, also called genital ligula, is on segment 2 and has an entirely different origin than the copulatory organ in dragonflies. One difference between dragonfly and damselfly mating is that many dragonflies perform sperm translocation before they attempt to mate, while the characteristic behavior of damselflies involves doing this *after* the female has been taken in tandem for mating. The reason for this difference is presumably that such behavior is possible in the way damselflies hook up to the thorax in tandem but more difficult in the way dragonflies hook up to the head. The origins of this difference remain unknown.

A female odonate has two options. She can refuse to participate in the next stage of mating because the grip doesn't feel right. The male appendages are usually species-specific in structure, and the parts of the female clasped by the male may be equally so. If the structures fit perfectly, she will respond positively, curving her abdomen forward and very quickly contacting his second abdominal segment, to be locked in place by the male's hamules and in position for copulation. Then copulation takes place, the male inserting his penis and transferring sperm into her vagina.

LEFT: *Orthemis* species copulate in flight for a matter of seconds, not having a need to land for this process as most other odonates do.

OPPOSITE: The connection in this pair of *Platycnemis acutipennis* involves four male appendages and the female thorax, fitting tightly so they can stay together in flight.

Copulation

Copulation has several stages. First, often accompanied by vigorous pumping action, sperm displacement occurs. This behavior is characteristic of the Odonata, especially damselflies and skimmers, and may occur in species of other dragonfly families. The penis of the male scoops or flushes out sperm deposited by a previous male. Thus if a female has mated but then is captured by a second male before she has oviposited, the first male's reproductive investment is lost. The penis of many odonates is adorned with scoops, flagella, and fancy brushes, not only for sperm displacement but also for species recognition. There may have been sexual selection: females mating with males that have a better displacement apparatus.

During the second stage of copulation, the male inserts his own sperm into the female's sperm-storage organs, the bursa copulatrix and spermathecae. In at least some damselflies, the male packs the bursa full of his own sperm, which then take precedence over the sperm from one or more previous matings. Partly because of this aspect of it, copulation can be a lengthy process, lasting up to several hours. Among damselflies, it often continues for 5–10 minutes but can be longer. Damselflies may remain in the wheel for hours, but copulation takes up a relatively brief part of that period. By staying hooked up, the male effectively prevents the female from another mating in which his sperm might be displaced.

Diversity in mating structures

However much the species may look similar to one another, they are anatomically different. The abdominal appendages of the males differ sufficiently to allow us to identify them by these. Similarly, the front of the pterothorax in female damselflies, where the cerci of the males press into the thorax during mating, has a pair of plates called mesostigmal laminae that are different in every species. These have to fit together with the male cerci in a way that works for both sexes. If the cerci fit more or less and the paraprocts, by resting on the prothorax, hold the two sexes together, the male will continue to attempt to mate, but if the connection doesn't feel right, the female will refuse to copulate. So there are both mechanical and tactile interactions that determine whether mating will proceed.

In some genera of damselflies, several or even many species occur at the same site. American bluets (*Enallagma*) are a good example, with up to a half-dozen species occurring together in ponds and lakes in northeastern North America. How do they keep their sex lives straight? Do males always know the correct females with which to attempt mating? The simple answer is that they don't. Experiments performed again and again show that many male damselflies will attempt to mate with any female they encounter of more or less the right size and color. Thus mismating can be common in these situations, but genetic incompatibilities usually prevent hybrid offspring.

Female choice

Although males take the initiative in grabbing a female for mating, nevertheless females have many options. They decide when and where to visit the water; they can copulate or refuse to do so; and they can oviposit immediately or leave the water and return at another time. In some species they apparently even have control of which male's sperm to use after multiple matings. Sperm from the most recent mating is in the bursa, but a female can move sperm from one of the spermathecae, which may have a mixture from several other males, to use it instead of the bursa sperm. We don't know how she knows which male would be the best sperm donor!

Avoidance of Mating

Male harassment of females

A female approaching the water is almost invariably detected by a male, and mating ensues. But because the sex ratio there is so skewed in favor of males, every female is the subject of pursuit, and a single female, even if fertilized and going about oviposition, is harassed unendingly by males other than the one with which she mated. Females have evolved many tactics for avoiding this. They often oviposit early in the morning or late in the afternoon, when few males are present. An ovipositing female may drop to the ground or even the water, not so much playing dead as avoiding the flight behavior that catches the male's attention. For a female to land on the water, full of odonate predators, shows the very strong pressure to avoid male harassment. But more extreme behavior has been frequently observed: a female may turn around and bite a male that has been trying to mate. In one case, a female Four-spotted Skimmer (*Libellula quadrimaculata*) bit a male repeatedly, causing it to drop motionless to the water, where a frog ate it!

Females appear in general willing to copulate if the male that clasps them is their own species. Some marked females have been reported to mate as many as a half-dozen times in a day. But females may not have to mate every day, as they store sperm in the bursa that can be released through the fertilization pore to fertilize eggs that pass. Different species of odonates have been found to store viable sperm for up to 15 days, allowing the females to fertilize up to at least 13 clutches of eggs laid on consecutive days. Some damselflies are thought to mate only once and presumably store sperm for their lifetime. Functionally, they fertilize themselves.

The presumed reason for avoiding harassment is the time wasted in additional copulations with still

other males. Copulation can be a lengthy process, more so in some species than others. It varies from just a few seconds in flight to several hours at rest. Lengthy copulation in some damselflies, for example, Pacific Forktail (*Ischnura cervula*), takes place in the afternoon, the female is effectively guarded from other males in that way, and she can oviposit early the next morning.

Female polymorphism

Polymorphism is the occurrence of more than one color morph in a species, the morphs being independent of sex and age. This phenomenon occurs widely in female pond damsels and darners in the temperate zone, with one morph dull (heteromorph, also called gynomorph) and the other with much blue and somewhat male-like (andromorph). The blue females are less likely to be

harassed by males of their species, indicating that they are effective male mimics. However, when they are the dominant morph, males apparently learn to recognize them and mate with them at high frequency. In addition, andromorphs are more likely to be attacked by visual predators, indicating the trade-off that characterizes such a system.

In many odonates, especially damselflies, the male stays attached to the female as they fly around looking for appropriate sites and then as she actually lays her eggs. This tandem oviposition is an effective way of preventing other males from mating with her. Although water bodies are usually rendezvous sites, in some species males encounter females well away from the water, hook up and copulate there, and then fly in tandem to the water to oviposit. This is often the case in species that remain in tandem to oviposit, for example, Common Green Darners (*Anax junius*), meadowhawks (*Sympetrum*), and many damselflies.

OPPOSITE: Females of *Ischnura verticalis* store enough sperm to fertilize all the eggs they produce and thus reject males aggressively.

TOP LEFT: The male *Ischnura cervula* stays in copulation for hours to protect his sperm investment.

TOP RIGHT: A male *Anax junius* shows interest in an ovipositing female *Rhionaeschna multicolor*.

ABOVE: Andromorphic female damselflies such as *Ischnura elegans* look enough like males that they are harassed much less by them.

Oviposition and Mating Success

Exophytic oviposition

Odonates have two very different modes of oviposition. In exophytic oviposition, a female drops her eggs into the water. The eggs are extruded from a genital pore at the end of the eighth abdominal segment, either singly or in clumps. In clubtails especially, females often rest while forming a sizable clump of eggs, then go to the water to deposit them. In many species, there is a subgenital plate (vulvar lamina), ranging in size from so short as to be barely visible to a substantial structure that extends to or beyond the abdomen tip, which allows the eggs to build up in a clump as they are extruded. Typically, the female in flight dips her abdomen tip into the water and releases the eggs.

An ovipositing female may hover in one spot, methodically depositing eggs that descend to the bottom or into vegetation, perhaps moving a short distance and doing it again, or she may fly rapidly over the water, striking it at intervals, sometimes long intervals, and scatter her eggs much more widely. Oviposition may last for several minutes, with more than 100 dips to the water in one bout in some species. Clubtail eggs have filaments that unwind and snag on the substrate as they float downstream. Female baskettails (*Epitheca*) produce huge egg masses heavy enough that they have to curl their abdomen up in flight as they search for just the right spot. The eggs come out in a long string, much like the eggs of toads, and snag on the vegetation.

Some dragonflies hover and drop their eggs from the air, this perhaps being a way to avoid predation by fish that lurk below. Some skimmers that breed in temporary wetlands even seem to breed on land, dropping single eggs to the ground. These low areas fill with winter rains and thus provide habitat for the larvae

TOP: Female clubtails such as *Ophiogomphus edmundo* extrude a ball of eggs while in rest, then fly to drop them in a stream.

ABOVE: A male *Plathemis lydia* guards his mate while she oviposits. He will attempt to chase away any intruding males.

that hatch from these eggs in spring. A few dragonflies are epiphytic ovipositors, depositing their eggs directly onto plants above the water surface, either in flight or while briefly perched. There is great variation within this general method, and each genus and even each species has its own specific method, depending on whether it is stream or pond breeding and on the amount of emergent and submerged vegetation.

Female guarding

During exophytic oviposition, males in the skimmer family usually guard the female with which they have just copulated. Because of what we now know of sperm displacement, the benefit of doing this becomes clear. Oddly, this noncontact guarding does not usually occur in the other families with exophytic oviposition, including clubtails, cruisers, and emeralds. Many skimmers oviposit rather sedately, staying in one place or moving short distances, while females of species in these other families typically fly around more rapidly and lay their eggs irregularly over a long flight path, making them less susceptible to disturbance by additional males as well as more difficult to guard.

In some skimmer species, for example, meadowhawks (*Sympetrum*) and pennants (*Celithemis*), the male remains in tandem with the female in a form of contact guarding. In these species, it appears that it is the male that seeks oviposition sites and controls the movements of the female, even dipping her down to the water to release eggs. Saddlebags (*Tramea*) have an unusual version of this, in which the male releases the female, she drops to the water to lay eggs, then he immediately recaptures her and they move to another spot, then repeat.

Tandem oviposition is unknown in dragonflies of other families except for a few darners (*Anax*) that oviposit in open areas where females would be very subject to harassment. Even these pairs are harassed by conspecific males attempting to break them up.

TOP & ABOVE: A tandem pair of *Sympetrum illotum* hovers over the water (top), then descends and the female lays a few eggs. They repeat this over and over.

But not all exophytic dragonflies drop their eggs in the water. For example, in spiketails (Cordulegastridae) the subgenital plate is prolonged into a pointed spike, forming a "pseudo-ovipositor" that is used to push eggs into a sandy substrate in the streams in which they breed. Some emeralds of the genus *Somatochlora* have a similar modification, and a few skimmers likewise, including some meadowhawks (*Sympetrum*) and all woodskimmers (*Uracis*). In *Uracis*, the "pseudo-ovipositor" pushes eggs into the soil, to hatch when the next rainy season floods the low area.

Endophytic oviposition

Odonates that oviposit endophytically have a real ovipositor, a complex organ at the end of the abdomen that is used to insert eggs into plant tissues. All damselflies have this, as do darners, petaltails, and redspots among the dragonflies. The ovipositor has a pair of serrated cutting blades that slice into the plant surface and a pair of styli (sing. stylus) that provide a tactile map of the substrate that is not visible to the forward-looking eyes. Females move up or down stems, making regular slits and depositing one or more eggs in them. The eggs of endophytic species are slender and elongate to fit their temporary homes; those of exophytic species are oval to round.

TOP: Spiketails are named for their enlarged and pointed subgenital plate with which females push eggs into bottom substrates in streams.

ABOVE: In *Erythromma lindenii* and many other damselflies, females and occasionally pairs back down underwater to lay eggs.

RIGHT: The ovipositor of a female damselfly.

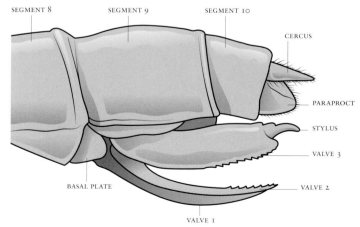

SEGMENT 8 SEGMENT 9 SEGMENT 10 CERCUS PARAPROCT STYLUS VALVE 3 VALVE 2 BASAL PLATE VALVE 1

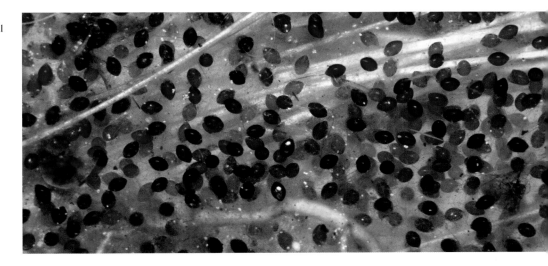

Clutch size

Clutch size is the number of eggs laid by an organism and can be expressed at a single instance, as the eggs in a bird's nest or the eggs a female odonate can hold in her abdomen at once and lay during a day's oviposition bouts. Female odonates produce and mature eggs almost continually throughout their lives but may lay a single clutch in a single visit to the water, then mature additional eggs for the next clutch. Maximum daily clutch sizes are commonly in the range of 100–700 in damselflies and 400–2,000 in dragonflies. The Four-spotted Skimmer appears to be the present record holder, producing 3,300 eggs in a clutch. It should not be surprising that exophytic species, which broadcast eggs, have clutch sizes much larger than endophytic species, which lay them a few at a time.

Surprisingly, females of different species can have very different clutch intervals—the periods between successive clutches. Females of some species lay every day, whereas others have intervals of up to five days or more, building up a larger clutch during that time. Laying every day could be a good strategy, as a female odonate might not survive another day to lay another clutch. However, the act of oviposition itself may be the most dangerous time.

Lifetime mating success

There is also a lifetime figure of egg production. As you might guess, these figures have not been established for most Odonata, but as they are insects, with no parental care and thus very high mortality of immature stages, the numbers must be quite high. Most female odonates, if they live long enough, lay more than one clutch. It may take at least a few days for a female to reconstitute a clutch, bearing in mind again that she can fertilize it with stored sperm. So a female with a clutch size of 400 could multiply that several times over in enough time. Species in which adults live for a month or more clearly have the potential to lay large numbers of eggs.

Female success can be measured in total number of eggs laid in a lifetime, and male success must be measured in total number of matings. By this criterion, a surprising number of males are completely unsuccessful. Several studies have shown great asymmetries in mating success. Many males of territorial species that do not successfully defend territories *never* mate, in some populations more than half of them suffering this fate. On the contrary, the most successful males may mate again and again, up to nine times in a day. Some males appear very worn-out at season's end.

Great Spreadwing
Archilestes grandis

Perching in the open over a stream and easily flushed, this damselfly is large enough to be mistaken for a dragonfly as it flies away. When it lands, its damselfly shape is evident, but the wings are outspread as in a dragonfly. Open wings facilitate a quick takeoff, this being appropriate in a species that feeds by sallying forth after small flying insects. Most damselflies rest with wings closed, but members of several families, especially in the tropics, have the open-wing habit. Closed wings are considered less conspicuous, and it makes sense for the smaller damselflies, with presumably more predators than the larger ones, to have evolved this wing position.

Great Spreadwings lay their eggs well up in tree branches, perhaps laying claim to the highest oviposition sites of any odonate, except of course those that are in phytotelmata well up in the trees in tropical forests. Perhaps the large size of the nine species of this genus is an adaptation to utilize woody substrates for the eggs, as it takes a larger and stronger ovipositor to insert an egg into a woody branch. Relatively few damselfly species do this, and this adaptation would allow these spreadwings to breed in habitats with little or no herbaceous vegetation. Such sites are found, for example, along small woodland streams that are inhabited by Great Spreadwings. This may be what has allowed the species of *Archilestes* to colonize North America, well north of their probable origin in Mexico and Central America.

The eggs of Great Spreadwings overwinter in the branches. When an egg hatches, the tiny prolarva flips out of it and drops to whatever substrate is below. Thus the eggs should be laid above the water of the stream, and it may be that by going higher in a tree, the branch is more likely to be over the water.

FAMILY	Lestidae
DISTRIBUTION	Across most of the southern United States, south in mountains to Colombia and Venezuela
HABITAT	Slow streams

2³⁄₁₆ in
5.6 cm

ABOVE & LEFT: Female Great Spreadwings have a strong ovipositor to facilitate laying their eggs high in a tree trunk, up to 44 ft (13.4 m) above the water.

Green Metalwing
Neurobasis chinensis

Fortunately for naturalists, this spectacular damselfly species is common and widespread in Asia. A male flying in the sun, green wings flashing, can elicit a gasp. Males open and close their hindwings at intervals as a signal of territory ownership. When they fly over their territory, they use only the forewings for propulsion and keep the hindwings wide open to display their brilliant upper surfaces. The stationary hindwings provide lift as well as display.

The brilliant green of the wings is a structural color, produced by their laminar surface. The lower surface of the wing is dark and opaque and absorbs light, but the upper surface comprises up to 11 layers of contrasting bands, light and dark, that reflect ambient light. Each reflected ray reinforces the others to produce the brilliant color we see. Both the brightness and even the hue change slightly with different viewing angles.

After mating, females submerge to oviposit in masses of rootlets extending into the stream from trees along the bank. The oviposition habits of many calopterygids depend on these trees, thus retaining forest cover on the banks of streams is essential to them. The eggs are slender, 0.03 x 0.006 in (0.75 × 0.15 mm), and hundreds of them are laid in aquatic vegetation. They are smaller than in related species in the temperate zone, and smaller eggs allow females to produce more of them.

The larvae of calopterygids are the most slender of any odonates and can hide easily in the rootlets. They are more active at night, when it is safer to be in the open in a fish-rich environment, and they can find their own prey by touch, facilitated by their long antennae and legs.

FAMILY	Calopterygidae
DISTRIBUTION	Widely distributed in southeastern Asia, from northeastern Pakistan to Fujian, China, south to southern India, Sri Lanka, peninsular Malaysia, and Sumatra
HABITAT	Forested streams of all kinds, rocky to sandy, from sea level to 6,600 ft (2,000 m), persisting in disturbed environments

2⅜ in
6 cm

RIGHT: **In the air with clear forewings beating, the male *Neurobasis chinensis* can hold open his electric-green hindwings.**

Black Velvetwing
Dysphaea dimidiata

Males of this damselfly species perch on emergent logs and branches of fallen trees in the sun over riffles in forest streams. They are rarely seen mating, and copulation is brief, then females oviposit solo in fallen logs underwater—an adult in its larval habitat. The males perch with wings closed, typical of damselflies, then suddenly open them and depress them to angles as much as 40° below the horizontal, much more drooped than any other damselfly species. This presents a very different appearance and is perhaps a display, although nothing has been written about male interactions. They are very visible from the side with wings closed, and from above or below with them open.

Of the nine species of *Dysphaea*, most have wings partially or entirely black, and the same behavior has been observed in several other species although not reported in the single species with brown wings, *D. gloriosa*. A Chinese species, *D. haomiao*, has been reported not only to perch with wings outspread but also to glide over a river much like an anisopteran.

Of almost 3,200 species of damselflies known, it will always be an interesting question as to why this single genus exhibits this peculiar dragonfly-like behavior.

The Euphaeidae includes seven other genera, and of them, an open-wing position, with wings elevated well above the thorax, has been reported in two, including the Odalisque (*Epallage fatime*) of southwestern Asia. In the genus *Euphaea*, with 30 species, only a few normally hold their wings open. All of the others, even those in which the wings are colored, perch with closed wings, and none of them achieves the droopy-wing position of *Dysphaea*. In damselflies at least, wing position seems to be readily modified to fit a situation, for example, the evolution of particular displays.

FAMILY	Euphaeidae	
DISTRIBUTION	Southern Thailand, peninsular Malaysia, and the Greater Sunda Islands (Sumatra, Belitung, Java, Borneo), also Palawan in the Philippines	1⅞ in 4.8 cm
HABITAT	Clear lowland forest streams and rivers with good current	

ABOVE & LEFT: The large, dark species of *Dysphaea* of southeast Asian streams alternate perching normally with, at times, depressing the wings as no other damselfly does.

Splendid Longlegs
Austrocnemis splendida

The three species of *Austrocnemis* are tiny damselflies with very long legs, with which they somehow jump into flight from the floating vegetation on which they usually perch. They may be found resting on a water-lily leaf with legs outspread, and when disturbed they seem to zip over to a nearby leaf. Although surely they are using their wings, their style of movement is very different from other damselflies on water lilies, which can be seen obviously to fly from leaf to leaf. *Austrocnemis* even perch differently, their long legs elevating them well above the plant surface. Perhaps this gives them a better view of the surroundings, where predators may approach. They remain on their leaves on windy days when other damselflies retire to dense vegetation, and they seem so well adapted to them that they may even spend the night on them.

Many parts of the world have damselflies that are strongly associated with water lilies (*Nymphaea* and *Nuphar*) and occur in no other habitat. In flight they stay very low over the water, presumably to avoid predation by both birds and larger odonates. In eastern North America the Lilypad Forktail (*Ischnura kellicotti*) is such a species. Characteristically, it rests on the big, flat leaf with abdomen curved downward to touch the leaf with the tip, this again being a behavior different from typical damselflies that perch up on stems and keep their abdomen perfectly straight.

On the other hand, male *Austrocnemis* often raise the blue tip of their abdomen slightly when they land, perhaps as a display. The metallic front of the thorax in this genus is also special, being found on very few small damselflies but shared by the unrelated sprites *Nehalennia* of the northern hemisphere. Are these similarities by chance, or do they constitute a pattern that we have yet to understand?

FAMILY	Coenagrionidae
DISTRIBUTION	Eastern Australia
HABITAT	Well-vegetated lakes, ponds, and slow-flowing streams

$^{13}/_{16}$ in
2.1 cm

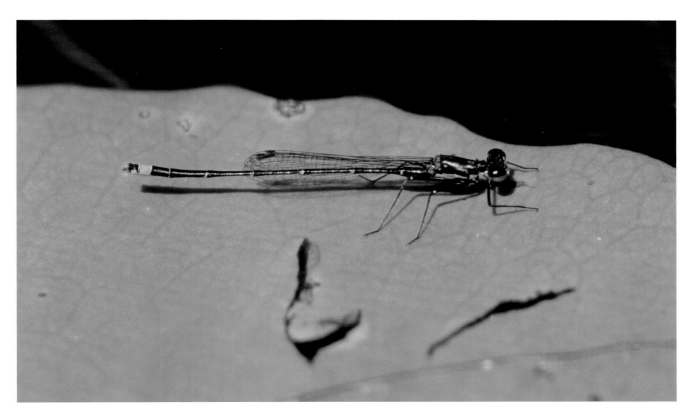

ABOVE: Small Australian damselflies of the genus *Austrocnemis* usually perch on flat leaves on the surface of a heavily vegetated pond; this is a male *A. splendida*.

LEFT: A female *Austrocnemis maccullochi* is standing up even higher. Individuals of this genus look as if they jump from leaf to leaf when they move.

Damsel Dragon
Epiophlebia superstes

This genus of three species has long occupied a puzzling position in odonate classification and it is currently placed in the suborder Anisozygoptera, closer to the Anisoptera than the Zygoptera. The wings are held either half-open or closed. Although the hindwings are slightly broader than the forewings, an anisopteran trait, the flight is more like that of a damselfly, and the adults never glide like dragonflies. The wing venation features crossveins similar to those in many Mesozoic fossils of the Anisozygoptera.

The larva looks just like an anisopteran, but it lacks the ability to move by jet propulsion, in that way being similar to zygopterans. We have a good fossil record of adult odonates, based to a substantial degree on wing venation, but venation has been shown to change with the evolution of different wing shapes so isn't especially useful for phylogeny. But we have even less of a fossil record that might show how the larvae of present-day families achieved their shapes and other adaptations.

Perhaps one of the more interesting things about this "living fossil" is its behavior, which is comparable to both dragonflies and damselflies in its cold-stream habitat. It is a spring species, with a highly synchronized flight season of no more than a month at the beginning of summer. Thus the larvae overwinter in the final instar, but after a very long development period of seven or eight years. With this long period, they go through 14 larval instars, which is a high number for an odonate. Males fly up and down their home river throughout much of the day if warm enough, this being observed at 54°F (12°C) or above in one study. If the air temperature is relatively low, the advent of clouds will cause them to leave the river, but if it is a warmer day, they fly during cloudy weather as well.

FAMILY	Epiophlebiidae
DISTRIBUTION	Japan
HABITAT	Swift, cold streams and rivers in hill country

2 in
5 cm

RIGHT: **Damsel Dragons** are odd relics of the past abundance of their group, with anatomy and behavior intermediate between damselflies and dragonflies.

Dark-saddled Darner
Gynacantha membranalis

This magnificent species is one of the largest Central American dragonflies. It is seen most often when one flies into a cabin or comes to a light on a house in or near the forest. It is a crepuscular forager, looking for insects at dusk and dawn and apparently confused by our drastic alterations of lighting conditions in its forest environment. During the day it hangs from a branch in the forest, dull enough at a distance to blend with the surroundings but quite colorful at close range.

The great majority of *Gynacantha* species are crepuscular foragers, called duskhawkers in the Old World. As the sun goes down and the light dims at the edge of the forest, out come these big dragonflies to feed. They fly back and forth, often along trails or other more open areas and from near the ground to well up into the canopy. It's difficult for us to understand how they can see their small prey at these low light levels, but they do. This must be facilitated by the crepuscular species having larger ommatidia than their day-flying relatives. Also, their head is about the same width as those of the day-fliers, but their face is narrower, giving them more eye surface and distinctly more ommatidia and better vision directly in front.

Nothing is known about mating in Dark-saddled Darners, but their larvae have been found in tree holes—crevices in trees that contain water during at least part of the year. The relatively large larvae are at the top of the food chain in such places, eating the larvae of damselflies and mosquitoes and even frogs that breed there. Of special interest, they are the only odonate species thought to breed both in and out of phytotelmata, having been seen guarding small pools and ovipositing in moist wood at ground level.

FAMILY	Aeshnidae
DISTRIBUTION	Nicaragua to Bolivia and Brazil
HABITAT	Rain-forest swamps

3⅛ in
8 cm

RIGHT: **This large species is common in neotropical forests, where it forages at dusk and dawn and breeds in surprisingly small pockets of water.**

Large Pincertail
Onychogomphus uncatus

This species is typical of its family—a dragonfly that lives in and along streams with clean water, a moderate current, and a gravelly, rocky bottom. The adults are well camouflaged, their outline broken up by repeated black and yellow markings. Males are not territorial, as there are no optimal oviposition sites to be defended, and at times they perch very close to one another. They rest on stones in the stream and at its margin, flying up at intervals to feed and cruising short distances to different perches. They fly toward any dragonfly of similar size that passes, both their own and other species, and this causes them to change perches often and eventually persist at a site with not so many other dragonflies, even if it is suboptimal to females.

Only a minority of passing dragonflies are female pincertails, with females being scarce enough at the water to mean that most male flights do not end in mating. When a female is encountered, a short chase ensues, and the male grabs her with his terminal appendages, which from their size and shape are clearly made for grappling. Copulation is away from the water and is a lengthy process, lasting 2.5–3.5 hours. Early in the morning and late in the afternoon, the sexes meet away from the water, and if mating occurs late in the day, oviposition is not until the following day.

There are many web-building spiders in vegetation near the water at some sites, and apparently the males cannot see them as well in low light levels, so many more of the dragonflies are caught in the evening than at midday. Mating away from the water is advantageous in such a situation. Both competition and predation act to modify the daily behavior of a dragonfly.

FAMILY	Gomphidae
DISTRIBUTION	Southwestern Europe and northern Africa
HABITAT	Shaded streams with moderate current, less often rivers

$2\frac{1}{16}$ in

5.3 cm

LEFT: Through precise embryonic development, the color pattern is repeated exactly on all middle abdominal segments, but the process must change on the shorter end segments.

BELOW: The camouflage of complexly patterned dragonflies is quite apparent in this male Large Pincertail. A passerby may notice it only when it flushes.

Common Shutwing
Cordulephya pygmaea

Among all the dragonflies, only this genus, with four species in Australia, and the South American sapphirewings (*Zenithoptera*) have the ability to close their wings after they first open them at eclosion. The sapphirewings have brilliant blue upper wing surfaces, so closing their wings is perhaps important for being hidden, and they can open them again for display. But the evolution of this peculiarity in the shutwings, the only other dragonflies that hold their wings closed among more than 3,000 species that hold them open, defies understanding. Nothing has been written about their habits that clarifies this behavior, although they have very narrow hindwings like damselflies, presumably facilitating the wing closing.

One possibility is that open wings are more conspicuous than closed wings. This has been put forth as an explanation for the closed wings of most damselflies, which are smaller than most dragonflies and are thus thought to be more subject to predation. Shutwings are quite small and actually look much like damselflies, but at close range their contiguous eyes and unlike forewings and hindwings give away their correct taxonomic placement. They perch on rocks and twigs in streams, perhaps the closed wings reducing territorial conflicts with dragonflies of other species that live on the same streams. They also tend to fly later in the season than other species, again perhaps to avoid conflicts.

If that weren't enough confusion, *Cordulephya* is in a group where there is still much uncertainty about taxonomic relationships among species. At present it is thought to be related not only to many Australian species but also to species scattered through Africa, South America, Asia, and even Europe—but no relatives in North America. As more species yield their DNA to science, this confusion will be a thing of the past.

FAMILY	Synthemistidae
DISTRIBUTION	Eastern Australia
HABITAT	Streams and rivers

1¼ in
3.2 cm

RIGHT: The Australian *Cordulephya* are the only dragonflies that perch with wings closed throughout their life, a puzzle to all who study dragonflies.

Eastern Pondhawk
Erythemis simplicicollis

This dragonfly species tells a story of success, increasing in recent years when so many other species are declining in our rapidly changing world. The secret to its success is global in significance: adaptation to anthropogenic changes. It thrives in any kind of still water, so the proliferation of borrow pits, mitigation ponds, farm ponds, ponds in city parks, and other constructed wetlands have favored its existence. These are habitats in which many other species cannot thrive.

Male Eastern Pondhawks begin their lives looking exactly like females in color pattern, being mostly bright green but with a black-banded abdomen. Over a period of two weeks, while foraging away from the water, they little by little turn blue from a deposit of waxy pruinosity exuded from the cuticle. The blue coloration first covers most of the abdomen and then the thorax. Very few male Eastern Pondhawks come to the breeding habitat before they have acquired their full color, and mature males remain there on average for 8–10 days, with a maximum of 45 days. The green

females come to the water and mate, copulating briefly and then, while guarded by their mate, usually laying a full clutch of hundreds of eggs within five minutes. They do not return to the water until they have matured a new clutch in the next few days.

The adults are very voracious, even for a dragonfly. They are the only common North American member of their family that regularly take other dragonflies as prey, up to their own size and occasionally larger. Cannibalism has been observed occasionally, which shocks onlookers more accustomed to vertebrates. Females are slightly larger than males by weight, and they tend to take larger prey, presumably to feed their energy needs while developing large clutches of eggs.

FAMILY	Libellulidae
DISTRIBUTION	Throughout eastern North America from southern Canada to Texas and Florida, south through Mexico to Costa Rica, and the Greater Antilles
HABITAT	Still and slowly moving water bodies of all kinds

1⅝ in
4.1 cm

LEFT: This male Eastern Pondhawk, colored just like the female when immature, has turned blue with maturity. It has captured a *Celithemis fasciata* in Texas.

LEFT: Eastern Pondhawks are among the most voracious of dragonflies, taking prey even up to their own size. This female has an *Argia fumipennis* in Florida.

Lucia Widow
Palpopleura lucia

These little dragonflies exemplify the African continent, their black-patterned wings showing up in ponds and other small wetlands south of the Sahara. They are joined in many of them by the very closely related *Palpopleura portia* (Portia Widow), a lookalike that has been considered the same species for most of their taxonomic history, the distinction finally being confirmed by genetic analysis. The two are readily separated by the different shape of the black markings in the wings of Portia wherever they occur together. Both species use their fancy wings in courtship displays, this being a common feature of small dragonflies with colored wings. A male will hover with wings fluttering in front of a perched female, in a display apparently essential to convince her to mate.

Even small odonates can live long lives. In an experiment that involved keeping numbers of them in captivity in a large naturally vegetated flight cage in Nigeria, a male of this species lived 48 days from emergence, and a female 52 days. In this group, both sexes reached sexual maturity in 10–14 days. Roosting was easily monitored in captivity, and individuals were seen to leave the water about two hours before they finally flew to a night-roosting spot. After brief preflight activities such as body-shaking, grooming, and wing-whirring, they left the perch before sunrise. After moving around the perching area for up to an hour or more, they finally flew to their breeding site at the water.

Further experiments on the larvae of this species showed that different amounts of prey availability influenced their development time greatly. Larvae on a full diet took 40 days to emergence, while those fed one-eighth as much food took 118.5 days. Apparently food shortage just slows them down on a genetically fixed pathway, as the size of the larvae at each molt was the same as their well-fed control counterparts.

FAMILY	Libellulidae
DISTRIBUTION	Widespread in sub-Saharan Africa
HABITAT	All wetland habitats with emergent vegetation, from lakes and marshes to slow-flowing streams and rivers

1⅛ in
2.8 cm

ABOVE: The dark markings in the wings of female *Palpopleura* make the wings look shorter and, together with the banded abdomen, may make them effective wasp mimics.

LEFT: Not only common and widespread but also beautiful, this small African species has caught the attention of researchers in molecular genetics, ecology, and behavior.

Violet Dropwing
Trithemis annulata

A dramatic success story, the Violet Dropwing has spread over almost all of Africa, where it is locally common in its preferred habitats. Sunlight and open air must be present; it is not a forest species. Lakes, ponds, and rivers of any sort are adequate, in its European range especially shallow waters that warm rapidly in summer; this would be important for a species of tropical origin. It has become ever more common in southern Europe, where human alterations of the landscape—opening up forests and constructing new freshwater wetlands—have favored colonization by this rapidly dispersing species. And it thrives on islands of all sizes, as long as they support fresh water.

To get an idea of the speed of dispersal in odonates of open landscapes, researchers dug a series of small ponds in the desert of western Namibia near a large river. By the next day after the ponds were flooded, individuals of this species and six others had shown up and began to mate and lay eggs. Larvae of three of them had emerged by the time the ponds dried up in 52 days, before complete larval development was possible in the other species.

In an analysis of 14 widespread species of African dragonflies for which complete larval development time is known, only four had more rapid development than *Trithemis annulata*, which was able to emerge in 52 days. Thus temporary water bodies lasting no more than two months during seasonal rains would support the larvae of this species and probably numerous others. This adaptation is particularly important in arid regions, where rainfall may be slight and scattered. On the other hand, oviposition in small, perhaps temporary water bodies is also a pathway to extinction when the rains are too few and far between.

FAMILY	Libellulidae
DISTRIBUTION	Far southern Europe, Middle East and throughout Africa, including Indian Ocean islands
HABITAT	Open ponds and lakes, slow rivers

1⅜ in
3.5 cm

RIGHT: **Known for its rapid larval development and high dispersal ability, this African species is very widespread. On a sunny day in Morocco, this male is obelisking.**

CHAPTER FOUR
The Life Cycle

Unlike advanced insects, odonates don't need a pupa to transform from the larva to the very different adult. Instead, they undergo their metamorphosis within the larva itself as it remains active in the freshwater community. The final stage is the emergence of the fully formed adult from its larval skin.

Larval Life

All adult odonates are surprisingly similar. All have big eyes, a robust thorax, long wings, and an elongate abdomen. The adult odonate shape has long evolved to be perfect at feeding on smaller organisms, avoiding predators, mating, and laying eggs, and so they all do the same thing in much the same way. The larvae are all carnivores like the adults, but where they live has brought about some surprising variation.

Basic larval anatomy

The larvae of the two primary suborders of Odonata are as distinctive as the adults. Anisoptera typically have compact bodies, although with much variation, with well-defined head, thorax, and abdomen. The legs are on the thorax, as in the adults, and just over halfway through development, wing pads begin to grow on the thorax and get larger with each molt.

Dragonfly larvae

One of the many special things about anisopteran larvae is their rectum. The rectum takes up much of the abdomen and fulfills three different functions. First, it is the posterior part of the digestive tract that stores lipids and glycogen, all digestion having been accomplished by the midgut. Second, it houses the gills in a complex structure called the branchial basket, which is the respiratory organ. The gills are easily seen in a dragonfly that has just molted, before its cuticle has become pigmented again. Water is drawn in through the anus and gas exchange takes place through the gills, with oxygen taken out of the water and carbon dioxide expelled back into it in the same airtubes—tracheae— with which adults respire.

Feces are enclosed in a membrane in the midgut, then pass through the rectum that way, so they don't

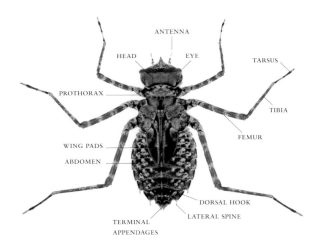

TOP: Larvae of darners or hawkers are the sleekest of all, with large eyes, slender body, catlike hunting, and a precision strike.

ABOVE: Anatomy of a dragonfly larva, *Macromia illinoiensis*.

foul the respiratory system. Because of the muscular diaphragm, water can be expelled very rapidly from the rectum, furnishing its third function, that of locomotion, as the larva can shoot forward to escape a predator by jet propulsion. Fecal pellets can be expelled ballistically, sometimes even coming out of the water if the abdomen is pointed upward at the surface.

Skimmers (Libellulidae) can be used as examples of larvae, varying from broader or narrower, more or less pointed toward the rear, hairier or smoother, and eyes larger or smaller and in different locations on the head. Among them they exemplify the four types: claspers, sprawlers, hiders, and burrowers.

Most are claspers on vegetation or sprawlers on an open bottom, and these tend to be smooth, without obvious setae, pointed toward the rear with long anal appendages, and with relatively large eyes on the sides of the head. Hiders among detritus and burrowers in the bottom substrate are narrower and hairier, with a square head with small, pointed eyes situated on either side of the front. Those eyes allow them to see when buried in mud and detritus, and the hairs gather material from the bottom for camouflage.

Species that live with predatory fish may evolve long lateral spines on either side of the abdomen tip, these differences even being evident within a species in the whiteface genus (*Leucorrhinia*). Experimental studies have shown that fish have a harder time handling spinier larvae.

Most families of Anisoptera have a labium that is somewhat spoon- or scoop-shaped, and when they capture prey it is at least partially engulfed, partially held by the broad, toothed labial palps that spread apart as the larva strikes. The labial "mask" (so-called because it covers the face) functions something like a catapult, with a locked lever storing kinetic energy that is then released for the rapid strike. In some families, for example, the burrowing spiketails (Cordulegastridae), the palps have jagged edges that are even more effective, perhaps in capturing larger prey.

Species in the family Macromiidae (cruisers) that sprawl on the bottom have evolved a flatter, more disklike body shape and long legs that act as prey detectors. When a leg is touched, the larva turns its head in that direction to be ready to shoot the large labium out to capture whatever is coming close enough.

Darners (Aeshnidae) are mostly claspers or hiders and have slender bodies that can move smoothly through vegetation and detritus. The head is large, with eyes bigger than in most other larvae. They are more active than some of their smaller relatives and may use jet propulsion more often. They also twist their abdomen to jab their long, pointed terminal appendages into anything that grabs them, including a human hand!

Aeshnids are active foragers, following potential prey with their large eyes and stalking slowly, just as a cat stalks a mouse. Their labium is flat and narrow and in some cases very long, extending well out in front of the head in a lightning-fast strike to capture the prey with long hooks that close when they make contact. Labium length varies greatly even within a genus, presumably correlating with different types of prey.

Clubtail (Gomphidae) larvae are typically slender and pointed toward the rear. They burrow just under the surface of sand or mud, the tip of the abdomen curved upward to be exposed to the water necessary for respiration. Extremes are shown by clubtails such as *Aphylla* and *Neurogomphus* that have the last abdominal segment extended into a long tube, necessary to reach the water as they burrow through soft mud. Many of the burrowing species eat midge larvae that live at that interface.

Some petaltails (Petaluridae) construct burrows in soft substrates, and the larva lives in the burrow by day and leaves it at night to forage for beetles and spiders. The burrows are usually soggy if not submerged, but the larva can extract oxygen directly from the air. Very few odonate larvae are completely terrestrial, moving about on the forest floor in wet tropical locations such as Australia and New Caledonia. They also respire through the rectum but must be in moist air.

TOP & MIDDLE: **Odonate larvae such as this *Aeshna* catch prey by shooting out the labium lightning-fast with hydraulic pressure from the abdomen.**

RIGHT: **This *Aeshna* larva has captured a metamorphosing froglet and has brought it back to the large, sharp mandibles that will chew it up to swallow.**

Types of larval labium in odonate families

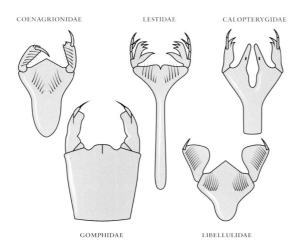

COENAGRIONIDAE   LESTIDAE   CALOPTERYGIDAE

GOMPHIDAE   LIBELLULIDAE

Damselfly larvae

Damselfly larvae are quite different, with their slender bodies and usually prominent caudal gills. Because at least the pond-dwelling species use those leaflike appendages to swim, their bodies cannot be broad and robust. They are all camouflaged by their coloration (most are brown, some green) and their slenderness, allowing them to blend with a plant stem. The most extreme adaptations for pond life are seen in the spreadwings (Lestidae), which have very long gills and in many cases an extremely long labium. Some of them are very active swimmers, living in open water and simulating a tiny fish at first sight. They presumably swim only to escape predators.

Larvae of stream damselflies typically have the caudal gills reduced and in some cases not functional as respiratory organs, when they could be called merely caudal appendages. Respiration in these larvae takes place at least in part within the abdomen as in dragonflies. Calopterygid larvae have very large antennae and clearly detect prey tactilely as well as visually.

Damselflies capture usually very small prey with a slender labium, somewhat spoon-shaped at the end and with a curved spine on each of the palps to facilitate prey capture. Lestids use their long labium much like aeshnids, to capture more distant prey with precision. In some species, the extended labium is as long as the body.

Communities of odonate larvae can be very diverse, and we know less than we should about how most of them interact in terms of predation and competition. Competition theory states that if two coexisting species are very similar in their niches, one should drive the other to extinction on a local basis, yet ponds and streams are full of congeneric species that seem to be doing much the same thing. Both microhabitat choice and differing seasonal patterns allow some avoidance, but much more research is necessary.

TOP: This *Lestes vidua* larva is slender, with long gills for rapid swimming and a long labium to capture prey well in front of the head.

ABOVE: Damselfly larvae respire through their large, flat caudal gills, and they rest with them open for maximum circulation.

Hatching and Growth

Eggs

Odonate eggs can develop very rapidly, hatching in five to six days in species that develop in temporary pools and are thus under strong selective pressure to grow rapidly. Often the larvae of these species show the most rapid growth of any odonates, including migrants such as gliders of the genus *Pantala*, darners of the genus *Anax*, and the widespread Tropical Bluetail (*Ischnura senegalensis*). Eggs of still other species show much more prolonged development of up to about eight weeks. Eggs reared in captivity develop more rapidly at higher temperatures, and this is surely duplicated in nature. Thus even the location where a female oviposits may be significant in the speed of development of her eggs and larvae.

Eggs may also show delayed development, in some species hatching being delayed until the spring following the autumn in which they were laid. Shorter days or low temperatures in autumn cause them to go into diapause, in which embryonic growth ceases. Hatching dates of as long as 250 days have been seen in eggs kept in aquaria. This occurs mostly in species that breed in temporary wetlands, which may be dry until filled with water by winter rains, by which time it is too late for the eggs to hatch until water temperatures rise again in the spring.

Prolarva

Eggs hatch into tiny prolarvae (or pronymphs) that look nothing like later stages. This stage may last only for seconds—long enough for the tiny creature to flip

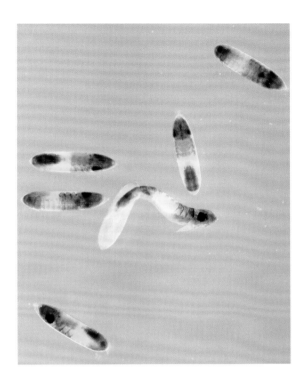

LEFT: An *Epiaeschna heros* prolarva emerges from its egg after 21 days. Others at the same stage of development are about to hatch.

BELOW: This just-molted libellulid larva shows the large gills in the rectum and the tracheal tubes that extend throughout the body.

itself about and, no matter where it begins, to end up in water, where it immediately molts into the first larval stage. Very often, perhaps in a secure setting, the prolarva molts immediately into the larva even as it is coming out of the egg. As the larva feeds and grows, its exoskeleton keeps it from enlarging, so it has to molt to become larger. The cuticle splits and a larger version emerges, takes in water to expand, and then hardens at a larger size in the next instar (larval stages are also called stadia). This molt goes on repeatedly until the larva is at its largest. Odonates vary greatly in how many larval instars contribute to reaching full size, varying typically from 10 to 15.

Length of larval life

Although most odonate adults live relatively short lives, the larvae of many species are very long-lived. The variation in development time is enormous. Some species that live in warm, temporary tropical wetlands can undergo larval development in no more than a month, living in the midst of great prey density and molting every few days. The migratory *Pantala* species are examples, as are others such as the Red-tipped Swampdamsel (*Leptobasis vacillans*) that was found to go from hatching to emergence in a newly filled marsh in Costa Rica in only 20 days.

At the other end of the variation, some dragonflies that live in cold streams at high latitude, such as the Damsel Dragon (*Epiophlebia superstes*), have been documented taking as long as eight years to undergo complete development. Each summer the larva grows a bit and molts only a few times, perhaps only once each year as it gets larger. Predation pressure must not be very heavy in such aquatic habitats for such extended survival to be possible. The adult life of a month or so is short relative to those years in the water, but it is sufficient for sexual maturation and reproduction, starting the cycle again.

Metamorphosis and Emergence

Complete metamorphosis in familiar insects

Most of the insects familiar to us, such as butterflies, beetles, wasps, and flies, have a four-stage life history: egg, larva, pupa, and adult. In these insects, when a larva reaches its full size it eventually becomes quiescent and constructs a case (chrysalis in butterflies, cocoon in moths) around it, when it becomes a pupa. The pupa is usually well camouflaged and/or in a protected place in which metamorphosis can take place within it. The larval tissues then dissolve except for small groups of cells called imaginal discs, so the pupa is largely liquid within. Then within this "pupal soup," the organs are reconstituted from the imaginal discs into new ones to make up the developing adult. When fully formed, the adult breaks out of the pupal skin, then as rapidly as possible dries out and hardens. Soon it will open its wings and fly away.

Pigments to bring about the definitive color pattern of the adult insect have not yet been deposited at this time, so freshly emerged adults are often pale. In fact, when you find a white insect, it is very likely to be freshly emerged rather than albinistic.

Incomplete metamorphosis in odonates

Odonate larvae are very different from other insect larvae. They undergo what has been called incomplete metamorphosis, although it seems quite complete when you compare the two very different-looking stages. But instead of occurring within a pupa, as in the moth or fly or beetle or bee, this metamorphosis takes place within the active final-instar larva. As the larva moves around the environment, feeding and avoiding being eaten, the adult body is forming within it. One change that can be seen is the increase in size of the wings, which are packed tightly within the wing pads of the larva. In later instars they become relatively larger, and in the final instar, the pads become swollen, this being an easy way to detect that this larva is fully grown and nearing emergence.

As these changes are taking place, the adult mouth-parts finally withdraw from the large larval labium, so that feeding is now impossible. Respiration begins to change from aquatic to aerial, and the larva spends a lot of time at the surface, even with its head or abdomen tip out of the water. Finally, it is time to leave the larval habitat and embark on the very different adult life. This is often called metamorphosis, but this is an erroneous term for this stage, as metamorphosis has already taken place. The proper term is eclosion, describing when an adult insect emerges from the pupa or, in this case, the larval skin.

Emergence

In a typical emergence, the larva crawls out of the water until it reaches an appropriate substrate. In most species, this is a vertical substrate such as a plant stem, a tree trunk, or a stream bank. There is much individual variation, but while some species may just clear the water surface, others climb well up into the trees, this perhaps being a safer emergence site than lower down. This site can also be flat sand or rock in some groups, especially the clubtails (Gomphidae). When the habitat is an open river or lake shore, far from vegetation, it is better for these diurnal emergers to get out of the larval skin quickly and fly away rather than to crawl a substantial distance to find an appropriate plant stem or tree to ascend. Correlated with this is the ability of gomphids to come out of the larval skin in an upright position, not hanging backward as is described below for most dragonflies.

LEFT: A dragonfly emerged from its larval skin moves fluids through its body, first expanding its wings as this one is doing, and then expanding its abdomen.

Eclosion

Once it has achieved its destination for eclosion, the larva rests for a while and its cuticle dries. Then it may swallow air or move fluids around in its body, and the thorax begins to swell. On the front of the thorax there is a tiny point that splits the larval cuticle, which opens up suddenly from the prothorax to the wing bases. The thorax continues to swell, exposing more of its sides, and the split extends onto the head. With more swelling and some muscular effort, the entire head and thorax then emerge from the larval skin. The wings are largely free from the larval skin at this point, as are the leg bases. Conspicuous white tubes extending from the thoracic spiracles are tracheae, breathing tubes pulled inside out because they have the same embryonic origin and are the same structure as the cuticle.

With a final effort, the odonate extends even farther from the larval skin, exposing the wings, legs, and abdomen base. If on a vertical surface, it is hanging backward. The legs move sporadically as muscles and joints come into full function. Then the dragonfly suddenly reaches up, if on a stem or trunk, or forward if on the ground, to pull itself completely out. The wings have been packed tightly in accordion fashion within the wing pads, and when freed, they begin to expand, starting at their bases. They expand to many times their original size as body fluids are pumped into them.

As the wings reach their full size, the fluid that has been pumped into them is recycled into the abdomen, expanding it to its full size. Then a few drops of excess water are extruded from the anus, and eclosion is just about done. The next step in a dragonfly is for the wings to open, which is the last time they will be

RIGHT: A clubtail dragonfly emerging on the shore of a large river does so fairly rapidly in the morning sun, this series of photos covering a period of 40 minutes.

closed in the great majority of species. Shortly the freshly emerged, soft and pale teneral will fly away on its maiden flight, to land in nearby vegetation or carry on over a longer distance. These teneral individuals will harden and color up fairly quickly, then they are considered immature until they attain sexual maturity and coloration.

ABOVE LEFT: **A damselfly has just come out of its exuvia, emerging with others of its kind and a dragonfly; the exuviae provide a record of their presence.**

ABOVE: **After developing in synchrony throughout the winter, thousands of pond damselflies, *Enallagma annexum*, emerge along a lake shore on a summer day.**

Emergence times

Most dragonflies emerge at night but wait until daylight and the warming of the sun's rays to undertake their maiden flight. On cool and cloudy days, that flight may be much delayed. Nocturnal emergence is surely to avoid predation by birds when the dragonfly is at its most vulnerable. There has been very strong selection for this, as can be seen just by watching birds at the waterside taking one teneral after another of species with daytime emergence.

At the highest latitudes, however, where it is too cold at night, dragonfly emergence is primarily in the daytime. Damselflies also usually emerge during the day, and this may be because eclosion is more rapid at higher temperatures, and this shortens the time at which they are vulnerable to a host of small predators, many of which—ants and spiders, for example—can capture them equally well day or night.

Exuviae

The cast skin of the larva is called an exuvia (pl. exuviae). These cuticular shells are left behind when the teneral flies away and may persist for long periods if not blown or washed away. Interestingly, some of them serve as important habitat for small spiders. Most of them are identifiable to species and thus become very important to researchers (see Chapter 5). One thing such collections have shown is that males may emerge earlier in some species, which would allow them to arrive at the rendezvous first to set up territories. In addition, by spending more time in their last instar and emerging later, females could become larger and thus carry more eggs.

Seasonality

Flight seasons

Odonates throughout their range have flight seasons—the period when adults are on the wing. This varies among species and regions. Many, but by no means all, species fly throughout the year in the tropics, while at higher latitudes some species have a flight season as short as a month. The periods of adult flight are somewhat regulated by larval development; this is called seasonal regulation. If a temperate-zone larva reaches the last instar by autumn, it overwinters in that instar and is ready to emerge as soon as water temperatures rise sufficiently in spring. These first emergers are often called spring species.

If all of the population is in that final instar, then the flight season is relatively short, with a synchronized emergence, in some species of clubtails (Gomphidae) and emeralds (Corduliidae) thousands of individuals emerging on the same day. These species also have a more or less synchronized die-off. For example, at a mid-latitude location such as the Carolinas in the United States, numerous species fly for less than two months in April and May. Species (and individuals) that overwinter in earlier instars continue growing in the spring as temperatures rise and then emerge later in summer. Temperate species that overwinter in the most instars have, as expected, the longest flight periods.

Tropical seasonality

In tropical regions, with temperature not a limiting factor, seasonality is more likely to be controlled by alternating dry and wet seasons. In Costa Rica, some lotic (stream) species have short (two-month) flight

BELOW: **In the temperate zone, temperature regulates midsummer peak presence. Precipitation does the same at a tropical locality, with a wet-season peak.**

OPPOSITE: **Some dragonflies emerge almost explosively in synchrony. These are** *Epitheca spinigera* **in Manitoba, Canada in June.**

1. Flight seasons of odonata in Washington state, USA

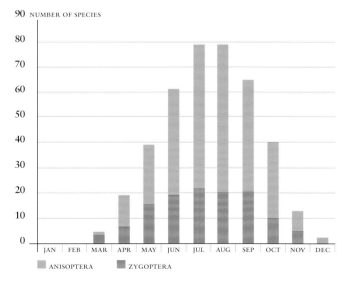

2. Flight seasons of odonata in Reserva Forestal Taboga, Costa Rica

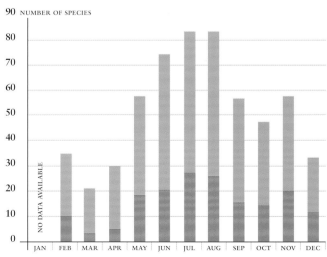

seasons at the beginning of the wet season (May to December), but how that is regulated remains unknown. Perhaps they remain in the final instar until water levels begin to rise, signaling the arrival of the annual rains, and then emerge at a time favorable to the adults.

A common type of seasonality is exhibited by many tropical pond and swamp species. Adults breed as wetland basins fill with water, and their larvae develop through the rainy season, emerging toward the end of it. Those adults then remain in favorable areas through a dry season lasting as long as six months, often withdrawing into the nearest forest. They are immatures in both gonad development and coloration, but are able to feed and stay alive for lengthy periods. As soon as the next wet season begins, they quickly develop mature gonads and coloration and go to the water to breed, beginning the cycle again.

The word "siccatation" has been coined to describe this passing of the dry season as an adult odonate.

It is the equivalent of aestivation and hibernation, when summer or winter are passed, respectively, in a nonbreeding and sometimes inactive stage. A few odonates fall into these other categories as well. For example, species are known that fly to woodland, often at higher elevations, in Algeria, Morocco, and Japan to escape the heat and drought of open regions in the lowlands, moving back to their breeding grounds in autumn. These species are migrants.

Hibernation

Odonates that overwinter as adults are more unusual. Although this has been called hibernation, they are not true hibernators as are some mammals at high latitude in which body temperature and metabolic rate decline independent of temperature. But the three species of the Eurasian genus *Sympecma* (Lestidae), called winter damsels, spend the winter as adults in a dormant state, as do occasional individuals of other species.

Dispersal, Migration, and Longevity

Dispersal

Odonates are among the best dispersers in the animal world, being comparable to birds. Anisopterans, especially the larger ones, cover long distances with their own powers of flight, while zygopterans are carried by prevailing winds. Some damselflies, especially the smaller ones, fly straight up into the air on their maiden flight and may be carried away by the wind. This may protect them from some predators, but it also allows them to disperse long distances like their larger relatives.

Quantification of dispersal abilities is difficult, as few odonates have been marked and then looked for at increasingly greater distances. Nevertheless, because of distances reached in migration, it is apparent they can fly many hundreds of miles. Dragonflies in arid regions leave their larval wetland, which may be drying up, and move across vast landscapes to find a new breeding site.

Trans-oceanic migration

Two African species, Vagrant Emperor (*Anax ephippiger*) and Keyhole Glider (*Tramea basilaris*), are slowly colonizing the eastern Caribbean and northern South America. Both have great dispersal powers and are helped in these travels by the prevailing easterly winds in equatorial regions. But some odonates move even greater distances. Several species have made it all the way to Hawaii, 2,400 miles (3,862 km) from California and 3,850 miles (6,196 km) from Japan.

Migration can occur at elevations of 3,000 ft (900 m) or more, and some blips detected on radar off Japan at night have been considered to be migrants, very likely Wandering Gliders (*Pantala flavescens*), the world-champion migrant dragonfly. This is the species that has appeared in flight over ships 600 miles (1,000 km) from shore.

TOP: Most adult dragonflies live only three or four weeks, and this female *Libellula forensis* with tattered wings is probably nearing that limit.

ABOVE: Thousands of *Aeshna mixta* roost in a field while apparently in migration in August at the mouth of the Danube River.

Migration in Common Green Darners

Dragonfly migration is still poorly understood, as there has been no success in tagging them individually and recovering the tags, as is routinely done with birds and was successfully done once with Monarch (*Danaus plexippus*) butterflies. But in autumn 2005, researchers tagged 14 Common Green Darners (*Anax junius*) with tiny radio transmitters in New Jersey. Most of them were tracked for some distance (from one mile to more than 80 miles/1–130 km) from the point of capture. Most of them flew on a southerly heading, they exhibited days of migration and days of stopover, they flew only when wind speeds were less than 15 mph (25 km/h), and they flew only on days when the previous night's temperature had been lower than the night before. Thus their migration strategy was much like that of birds in the same area.

This species is by far the best-known North American migrant odonate. At one time it was thought that there were two different populations, a migratory one and a resident one, but no genetic differences could be found between them. It appears likely that individuals that emerge early enough in the summer at high latitudes breed locally, while those that emerge later are stimulated to migrate south. Similar migration strategies known for the Vagrant Emperor, Wandering Glider, and Red-veined Darter (*Sympetrum fonscolombii*) in Central Asia indicate that this is a worldwide phenomenon among odonates.

Longevity

Enough studies have been done with marked adult odonates to tell us something about their longevity. Different damselfly species have been recorded with average life spans of 4–23 days after sexual maturation; dragonflies 7–38 days. The longest life spans for 23 species of Zygoptera range from 15 to 77 days and for 30 species of Anisoptera from 17 to 64 days (figures are from males, which are captured, marked, and resighted much more than females). Thus the smaller damselflies, surprisingly, can live as long as their larger relatives.

TOP: Great numbers of *Anax junius*, even tandem pairs, move southward every fall from southern Canada to northern Mexico and the West Indies.

ABOVE: Many tropical dragonflies survive from one rainy season to the next. This *Anatya guttata* with algae growing on its wings may be such an individual.

In fact, the longest recorded adult life span has been found in a damselfly—a Blue-winged Helicopter (*Megaloprepus caerulatus*)—that was recovered 180 days after being marked at emergence in Panama. A half year may be near the maximum for any odonate, but it may not be that unusual in the tropics, where many species stay alive as immature adults from the end of one rainy season to the beginning of another.

Common Winter Damsel
Sympecma fusca

The three species of this genus are unique among odonates in overwintering as adults. Although this is not true hibernation, as in mammals, it is quite comparable ecologically. The body temperature of insects rises and falls with environmental temperature, and thus they are dormant at very low temperatures. In almost all temperate-zone odonates, overwintering is in the larval or egg stage, usually under water and safe from terrestrial predators as well as the climatic extremes possible above the water surface.

But winter damsels have a life history more like some terrestrial insects, many of which overwinter as adults in protected locations. Overwintering as an adult allows very early breeding in the spring, and it can be advantageous to get an early start. *Sympecma* is the first odonate to be seen at the water in spring in western Europe, even before many of the migratory birds—all potential predators on adult damselflies—arrive from the south. Copulation takes place, eggs are laid, and the overwintering adults die, the next generation developing in the water. Those larvae emerge in mid to late summer, soon after the last overwintering adult has died. Thus adults are present almost the entire year. Tenerals have been seen in March and September, so in some areas there might be two generations in a year.

In the autumn, winter damsels find a sheltered spot in nearby woodland to cling tightly to the substrate and chill out. They are sometimes found in winter covered by a layer of frost, but inside the frost is a live damselfly waiting for the spring. Although most members of their family perch with wings outspread, the winter damsels do not, and this is very likely an adaptation to make them less conspicuous to birds. Nevertheless, they suffer moderately high mortality from rodent predation.

FAMILY	Lestidae
DISTRIBUTION	Southern and central Europe east to central Asia
HABITAT	Still water with much aquatic vegetation, especially with floating plant stems

1⁷⁄₁₆ in
3.6 cm

ABOVE: A winter damsel may spend the winter like this, exposed on a plant and dormant in the cold. Individuals are even found with frost on them.

LEFT: In spring winter damsels are active earlier than other odonates that are just emerging and even before most migratory birds, potential predators, arrive from the south.

Glistening Demoiselle
Phaon iridipennis

When a male of this species, the largest damselfly in much of Africa, flies over a stream, the wings flash brilliant blue or green. Yet when the same individual perches again low in the shade, it shows only a metallic green and brown body. In fact, it is one of the dullest of its family, which is full of stunningly colored damselflies. But the two species of *Phaon* show the same superb adaptation that many kinds of animals do: dull for camouflage when that's appropriate and bright when the time comes for display.

In a study in Kenya, male *Phaon* perched over a stream adjacent to an appropriate oviposition site and flew toward conspecific individuals. If the intruder was a male, the resident hovered over him briefly and the intruder opened and closed his wings slowly and raised the tip of his abdomen, showing the pale underside. The intruder usually flew away, chased by the resident. If a female, she opened her wings but did not raise her abdomen tip. The male landed on her wings and worked his way forward to attach his terminal appendages.

The pair then copulated for several minutes, and the female either left or began ovipositing immediately.

In the Kenya study, females oviposited in the bracts and stems of the sedge that was common there. Often multiple females came to the same spot, and the male effectively guarded them against other males, unless he was driven away. Oviposition lasted about an hour, with up to five females in one place. Females had two oviposition strategies. In sedge bracts, they laid eggs singly two at a time, then moved a short distance and did it again, this being behavior typical of many ovipositing damselflies. In the much harder sedge stems, they cut long slits and laid a closely packed row of up to 91 eggs.

FAMILY	Calopterygidae
DISTRIBUTION	Widespread in sub-Saharan Africa
HABITAT	Shaded rivers and streams

2¾ in
7 cm

ABOVE & LEFT: This large stream damselfly occurs in many parts of Africa. The blue flash on the male's wings (above) is due entirely to the structure of the wing membrane.

Phoenix
Pseudolestes mirabilis

It is very unusual for an animal with flight powers to be restricted to a continental island of any sort, in this case just 11 miles (18 km) from the mainland of China. Hainan has an area of 12,700 square miles (32,900 km²) and a human population of more than nine million. Fortunately for *Pseudolestes*, the largest settlements are along the coast, and there is much forest remaining in the interior, so it remains common in elevated parts of the island. Nevertheless, this damselfly is of great conservation concern as it is the only representative of its family, isolated genetically from any other odonate group, and with unique characteristics in both adult and larva.

Because of this, it has been well studied by researchers in recent years and found to have striking behavior. Both sexes have hindwings shorter and broader than the forewings and largely colored. Males have unique high-density white waxy fibers secreted by veins on the underside of the hindwing both at the tip and in a central area that looks bright golden or coppery from above. The white reflective surface thus produced greatly enhances that color. The black outer wings add to the contrast.

Males display aggressively to one another by hovering in midair with clear forewings beating and stationary hindwings open and the white underside directed toward the recipient. An elevated abdomen and bright blue face enhance the display. Males have been observed to hold the display position for up to four minutes, occasionally and briefly moving hindwings up and down. Even the perching of this species is unusual, with both sets of wings held backward at about 45°, something like a hawk moth (Sphingidae).

Females oviposit into wet wood at stream borders. This oviposition substrate is used in streams by numerous odonate species everywhere in the world in the absence of live aquatic plants.

FAMILY	Pseudolestidae
DISTRIBUTION	Hainan Island, China
HABITAT	Stony montane forest streams

1⅝ in
4.2 cm

ABOVE: The female Phoenix has fore- and hindwings quite different, yet she does not display. Perhaps constraints of embryonic development dictate the same wing shape for both sexes.

RIGHT: Male *Pseudolestes* in display flight on a Hainan Island stream, with beating forewings and stationary hindwings. Only a few other damselflies can perform this aerial feat.

Common Bluet
Enallagma cyathigerum

This large North American genus has only a few representatives in Eurasia, but this small damselfly species with only one or two generations in a year has colonized a post-glacial range over an area greater than 10 million square miles (27 million km²) and a linear distance of more than 6,000 miles (10,000 km). In Asia it is restricted to the taiga biome, not extending south into the Mongolian steppe and deciduous forests of China and Japan.

Careful studies carried out on this species using marked individuals showed that mortality of males occurred at a constant rate after sexual maturation. The mean length of reproductive life was 12 days, with a maximum of 39 days. Individuals occurred at high densities, with very little aggressive behavior, and only a fifth of the individuals remained in the same sector of a pond where they were first marked. Dispersal around a pond was due more to exploratory movements than to any direct interactions among individuals.

Many females oviposit underwater, descending as much as 39 in (1 m) and staying down for as long as an hour. A layer of air trapped around the body, perhaps by the fine hairlike setae all over it, provides oxygen for the underwater period. It is used up slowly, and some females have been recorded as spending an hour underwater. Some of them climb out of the water, but many just release their hold on the vegetation and pop to the surface from their own buoyancy. They are very likely to be stuck there in the water meniscus, but males are usually perched or hovering nearby, and one of them—often her mate—will take her in tandem and lift her from the water. He is rewarded by another copulation with a female that usually contains at least some unfertilized eggs.

FAMILY	Coenagrionidae
DISTRIBUTION	Across all of Europe and northern Asia from the UK to Kamchatka, also the Atlas Mountains in Morocco
HABITAT	Ponds, lakes, and slow streams and rivers

1⁵⁄₁₆ in
3.3 cm

ABOVE & LEFT: *Enallagma cyathigerum*, with brown or greenish females (above) and bright blue males (left), exemplifies the marked sexual dimorphism present in pond damsels and the majority of Odonata.

Blue-winged Helicopter
Megaloprepus caerulatus

This spectacular damselfly could be called, by wingspread, the largest odonate. A denizen of rain forests, it can be easily seen at scattered locations where biological field stations or ecotourism lodges provide access to its preferred habitat. Spend some time at one of these places and you'll eventually come across one, looking as if it has rotary blades as it crosses a sunlit clearing anywhere from ground level to well up in the canopy. The wing strokes are out of phase, thus the windmill effect, enhanced by the iridescent blue-black spots at the tips.

This species and its relatives, widespread in the New World tropics, are specialist predators on spiders, plucking them from the center of their webs in the forest. It has been speculated that as they hover in front of a web, the contrasting patterns on their wingtips mesmerize the spider, which doesn't try to escape until it's too late. These same wingtips may have the same effect on a scientist wielding an insect net or a jacamar swooping after it from a perch.

Helicopter damsels are spread through the forest, independent of the wetlands that support the majority of their relatives, because they breed in elevated water pools called phytotelmata. Some of them breed in bromeliads, which have long, slender leaves that grow out from a central base; rainfall funnels water into a central area that contains it, serving as habitat for frogs, salamanders, and numerous insects, including these damselfly larvae. Others, including *Megaloprepus*, don't breed in bromeliads but inhabit tree holes that fill with water during the rainy season. Because the holes contain different amounts of water, the food supply for the larvae is very variable, and the great variation in size of the adults comes from the size attained by the larva before it emerges.

FAMILY	Coenagrionidae
DISTRIBUTION	Eastern Mexico south through Central America and northwestern South America
HABITAT	Primary rain forest

3–4½ in
7.5–11.5 cm

RIGHT: *Megaloprepus caerulatus*, with the largest wings of any odonate, hangs vertically when not flying through neotropical forest clearings to catch spiders.

Giant Petaltail
Petalura ingentissima

There is general agreement that this species is the largest odonate; someone unfamiliar with *Petalura* might use the word "monster" on first sighting. It is only slightly larger than a few other Australian giants in the same genus, but the females, which are larger than the males, can have a wing span of 6⁷⁄₁₆ in (163 mm). They are distributed through most of Queensland's rain-forest belt, both lowland and tableland, but usually in relatively flat areas where muddy seeps form along forest streams. Males perch over these streams with hanging abdomen or fly up and down along them—both effective tactics in searching for females.

Females are usually found in areas appropriate for oviposition, where soft boggy mud occurs at the edge of streams. After a lengthy copulation and insemination of her eggs, the female comes to the water and probes the mud with her abdomen, in some places to a depth of its entire length. She is trying to find the best location for a clutch of eggs. Although she has an ovipositor for endophytic oviposition, she lays her eggs into the mud.

When the eggs hatch, the larvae begin to burrow through the mud. They form lengthy burrows and live in them for the rest of their larval life. There may be an opening into the water and another onto land, but they are terrestrial predators, coming out of the burrow at night to feed on other insects and spiders. When they finally emerge, they climb well up into the trees, and their large (2½ in, 63 mm) exuviae may be the only sign of their presence, as the adults are not often seen. Probably only a few larvae live in each of these limited muddy spots.

FAMILY	Petaluridae
DISTRIBUTION	Northeastern Australia
HABITAT	Rain-forest streams

4⁵⁄₁₆ in
11 cm

RIGHT: A female *Petalura ingentissima* at Mission Beach, Australia. This species is thought to be the world's largest odonate.

Common Sanddragon
Progomphus obscurus

Adult clubtails are not known for their fancy colors, although they do have fancy patterns, with a pale background color of gray or green or tan or yellow marked with brown or black. The many different genera differ in abdomen shape, from cylindrical to somewhat expanded to widely flared near or at the tip, giving a more or less clubbed look that gives them their name. Many of them are uncommon because they have rigid habitat preferences that stem from their relatively restricted larval habitat. The larvae of most of them are burrowers, specialized for different substrates and different current speeds.

This New World genus of dragonfly, with 69 species, is the largest in its family. Exactly as their name implies, the species are associated with sand-bottomed streams, rivers, and lakes, and their larvae are specialized for burrowing in sand. Mud and silt and even gravel are common substrates for other types of clubtails, but sanddragons need sand, for which they are highly adapted, and this makes the larvae look different from those of other clubtails. The larva is smooth and streamlined and built like a tank in front; this bulk is good for pushing through sand, which gives more resistance than mud. The front legs are highly adapted for burrowing, with all segments relatively thick. Comparisons with the front limbs of a mole are appropriate.

The antennae, essential to all odonate larvae as chemoreceptors, are thick and short and pointed forward to slide between sand granules. The wing pads, centered on the abdomen in most dragonfly larvae, are splayed out to the side in this and some other clubtail genera. Here they are protected from abrasion by being behind the legs. A *Progomphus* larva taken from the sand can burrow back into it almost instantaneously.

FAMILY	Gomphidae
DISTRIBUTION	Eastern North America from southern Canada south to Texas and Florida
HABITAT	Sandy rivers, streams, and lakes

2 in
5 cm

ABOVE: Sanddragons such as this *Progomphus obscurus* are usually found perched on sand, the habitat suitable for their aquatic larvae. Their mottled coloration makes them well camouflaged.

Common Baskettail
Epitheca cynosura

Baskettails are dull members of the emerald family of dragonflies, only their bright green to blue eyes indicating their relationship. They deviate also in their egg-laying apparatus and behavior, as well as the appearance of their eggs. Female baskettails have prolonged, forked subgenital plates (the "basket") that project backward far enough to hold a large ball containing 100 or more eggs. When a female produces a ball, she flies over the appropriate aquatic habitat back and forth, searching for just the right oviposition site.

Finally she drops to the water surface and drags her abdomen through it for several inches until it contacts a structure such as a submerged plant stem, at which time her clutch of eggs is pulled from her abdomen. The expansion of the jelly mass is remarkable, producing a string of eggs 4 in (10 cm) long and about ¼ in (6 mm) wide. A single egg mass may contain well over 1,500 eggs, with up to a dozen eggs present in any cross section of the string. Good oviposition sites may be scarce, as very often additional females will lay in the same spot, so that thousands of eggs are laid in a large, amorphous mass by as many as 15 females. One such clump was estimated to contain 110,000 eggs! No eggs are added on subsequent days.

The larvae of this species and several others in the genus are among the most highly synchronized in growth of any odonates. The development time is about a year, and the adults emerge in the following spring almost explosively, with hundreds or even thousands appearing on the same spring day when weather conditions permit. This is a good evolutionary strategy to combat predation, as there is insufficient time for predators to converge on such a spectacular emergence before most of the baskettails have flown away.

FAMILY	Corduliidae
DISTRIBUTION	Eastern North America from southern Canada to Texas and Florida
HABITAT	Open ponds and lakes

1⅝ in
4.1 cm

Common Baskettails forage
and defend territories and
lay eggs in flight, but
between flights males
(top) and females can be
seen basking on nearby
vegetation.

Seaside Dragonlet
Erythrodiplax berenice

Odonata are freshwater animals. The group surely evolved in freshwater wetlands, and almost all species occur in such habitats. A very few have become terrestrial, but the Seaside Dragonlet is the only one that has become thoroughly adapted to a saline environment (a few tropical species around the world live in brackish water). Its extensive range is mostly coastal, and it occurs over thousands of miles of coastlines in the Americas.

These dragonlets occur in any marine near-shore environment with vegetation in the water, including salt marshes in the temperate zone and mangrove swamps in the tropics. They are the only dragonflies that breed in the same habitats as saltmarsh mosquitoes (*Aedes*), and although they eat them, they unfortunately don't control them. They also live with other insects adapted to the sea, as well as occurring with a variety of shrimps and crabs and other strictly marine animals. Many of the species that occur in these habitats are euryhaline, being adapted to both fresh and salt water, and the dragonlets can also breed in fresh water when

heavy rains greatly reduce the salinity of near-coastal waters. With no competition from other odonates in its breeding habitat, *Erythrodiplax berenice* is sometimes very abundant.

A separate population of this species thrives in saline desert ponds in west Texas and New Mexico. Presumably being salt-adapted fits these dragonflies for colonizing this somewhat different environment hundreds of miles from the nearest populations on the Texas coast. One odd thing about the species is that while other *Erythrodiplax* oviposit solitarily, this one does so in tandem. Perhaps the unusual nature of its breeding habitat has selected for pairs to get together whenever they meet, even at some distance from the perfect spot. Such tandem pairs are often seen in flight, traveling substantial distances while hooked up.

FAMILY	Libellulidae
DISTRIBUTION	Nova Scotia to Venezuela and Trinidad along Atlantic, Gulf, and Caribbean coasts and throughout the Caribbean; also the Pacific coast of Mexico and the drainage basin of the Pecos River in Texas inland to New Mexico
HABITAT	Salt marshes and mangrove swamps, saline ponds in interior regions

1 5/16 in

3.3 cm

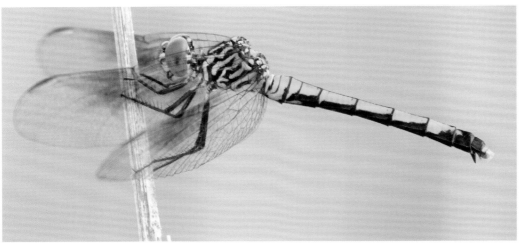

ABOVE: Seaside Dragonlets spend their time in saline environments, with no competition from other dragonflies. The black males defend territories in salt marshes and mangrove swamps.

LEFT: Female Seaside Dragonlets oviposit in water as salty as the ocean, and their larvae may be found in habitats with crabs, shrimp, and even sea urchins.

Wandering Glider
Pantala flavescens

This dragonfly species, also called Globe Skimmer, flies between the Indian subcontinent and eastern Africa and is seen in great numbers on the Maldives in between. Its movements through this area are so dramatic that they prompted the attention of a biologist who was intrigued to see so many dragonflies appear all at once on his home island. With great determination and a circle of friends and colleagues to be contacted all around, he established that the millions of dragonflies of this species that he was seeing are part of an amazing life story.

Every year, several generations of *P. flavescens* fly around the western Indian Ocean, each generation of adults traveling on the monsoon winds toward low-pressure areas where rain is falling, the rain forming shallow pools that are the breeding habitat of this species. In this great migration, they move in a circuit of 10,000 miles (16,000 km) southwest through India and the islands of the western Indian Ocean down to East Africa, then back around to the northeast to India again.

A small but significant number of bird species make the same migratory crossing in autumn, flying up to about 8,000 ft (2,500 m) above sea level on these dependable winds. Among them are falcons and rollers and bee-eaters that are well-known predators on dragonflies.

But this is only part of the story of this most widespread odonate species, present on all continents but Antarctica and most oceanic islands and surely dispersing among them. It has even reached Easter Island, where it is thought that the population has become resident and developed genetic and morphological differences. It is surprisingly rare in Europe, unlike its status at similar latitudes in North America. The combination of the Sahara Desert and the Mediterranean may be enough to prevent regular immigration north of that barrier, even for such a wanderer.

FAMILY	Libellulidae
DISTRIBUTION	Worldwide, absent from high latitudes
HABITAT	Breeds in shallow ponds, in flight everywhere

$1^{15}/_{16}$ in
4.9 cm

RIGHT: Wandering Gliders are world-class dispersers, in the air for weeks at a time. They fly over all the tropical oceans and reach the most distant islands.

Large Woodskimmer
Uracis fastigiata

The seven species of *Uracis* are common in the forest understory where they occur, and they epitomize the life history of tropical-forest dragonflies. Adults come together to mate in pools and even puddles formed on the forest floor when the first rains come. Males defend these sites against other males and mate with any female that arrives at the rendezvous. A true ovipositor like those in damselflies and darners is lacking in this family, but the female deposits her eggs in the wet mud with the aid of an elongated and pointed subgenital plate, which could be called a "pseudo-ovipositor."

The eggs hatch quickly, and the larvae grow rapidly in the shallow pools, which retain water as the rainy season progresses. Within a few months, they are ready to emerge, and the forest becomes full of woodskimmers, dull in coloration and sexually immature. In areas with a single relatively short rainy season, these immatures then remain in the area, feeding and avoiding predators, through the entire ensuing dry season. When the following rainy season finally appears, they quickly become sexually mature, and the body color of males changes from brown to pale blue, signaling that they are in fact ready to breed.

The presence of immatures and matures at different times during the year, the lack of any breeding habitat for as long as six months, and the frequency of breeding observed at the beginning of the rains all point to this scenario, even though there is no direct evidence (for example, individuals marked at the end of the rainy season that were found again at the beginning of the next one). That they live a long time, however, is indicated by the algae often present on the wings of mature individuals, this being a rather unusual condition in dragonflies.

FAMILY	Libellulidae
DISTRIBUTION	Lowlands of Guatemala south through Central America to Bolivia and Brazil
HABITAT	Tropical rain forest, both primary and second growth

1½ in
3.8 cm

ABOVE: Large Woodskimmers are among the most common dragonflies seen along trails through rain forest in the New World tropics, easily recognizable by their black wingtips.

LEFT: Female *Uracis* have subgenital plates extended into a point and jab their eggs into muddy forest pools. Algae on the abdomen are a sign of great age.

CHAPTER FIVE
Dragonflies and People

Dragonflies have seemed mysterious and unsavory to some cultures, symbols of light and happiness to others. With their diurnal habits, large size, bright coloration, and fascinating behavior, they are icons for the conservation of freshwater wetlands. In addition, they are also iconic throughout our popular culture.

Dragonflies in Our Culture

Red dragonfly—
are you here to lead us
to enlightenment?
Kobayashi Issa, 1823

Dragonflies are very much part of our popular culture. Depictions of them have become commonplace as jewelry and decorative items. Look at a group of people, perhaps best at an entomological meeting, and check out earrings, pins, and other jewelry. Odonata are often featured on lamps, plates and mugs, and clothing of all sorts. The very name is used again and again in commerce. There is dragonfly macramé, dragonfly fishing lures, dragonfly fibers, dragonfly software, a dragonfly movie and dragonfly theaters, dragonfly healing centers, dragonfly massage therapy, and innumerable others.

Odonate mythology

There is a rich mythology about odonates. Their names in many different languages and cultures tell a lot about how they are viewed, and in many parts of the world they are not viewed all that well. In Latin America *caballito del diablo*—"little horse of the devil"—is a common name for them. In the eastern United States, "snake doctor" (bringing snakes back to life) and "Devil's darning needle" (sewing the mouths shut of bad children while they slept) don't have much better connotations. In Norwegian, dragonflies are *Øyenstikker*, meaning "eye poker."

"Horse stinger" is another pejorative used widely in English-speaking countries because dragonflies are often seen around horses that are acting up. In fact, the dragonflies are probably there to feast on the horse flies, horse biters, that are the true culprits.

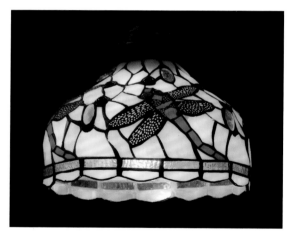

TOP: The dragonfly features on the two-and-a-half dollar coin of the Dutch island of Sint Eustatius in the Caribbean.

ABOVE: Dragonflies are unique shapes in nature and are thus easily represented in art, such as on beautiful Tiffany-style lamps.

Favorable attitudes

But many view odonates through much more approving eyes. They are revered in Japan, which was once called Akitsushima (meaning "islands of the dragonfly"). Native American myths hold that dragonflies represent swiftness, illusion, and change, and these features are attributed to them in other cultures as well. Dragonflies have been thought to bring good luck in China and other countries and have been used in love spells. It is not clear how much damselflies play a part in these beliefs and attitudes.

One of the ways dragonflies are loved—and this is not uncommon in Asia and known from Mexico and Madagascar—is as food. In Bali they are captured in flight at the end of a slender strip from a palm that has been dipped in the sticky sap of a jackfruit tree. They are then fried in coconut oil and eaten like candy.

Amateur naturalists

Interest in dragonflies among amateur naturalists has continued to rise with the advent of colorfully illustrated field guides for many parts of the world. Only in recent years have many species received common names in English and other languages, this apparently being a prerequisite for amateur engagement. Just a few decades ago, all identification guides were technical keys to specimens in the hand, but now they are profusely illustrated with paintings or color photos from life and allow identification of most species in the field through binoculars. The advent of digital photography has produced an online collection of thousands of beautiful photos of Odonata, and a search for almost any species is likely to produce images of it. Numerous websites are devoted to the Odonata at both professional and amateur levels (see Further Resources).

Dragonflies as spies

But there is much more of interest about dragonflies beyond what most of us see. Understanding the fine details of dragonfly flight, for example, has been a goal

ABOVE: The rich colors of *Celithemis elisa* will catch the eye as it perches or hovers at the water's edge.

BELOW: Some cultures find dragonfly larvae as tasty as the shrimp sold with them in a Chinese market.

among biologists for a long time, but more recently researchers have tried to mimic it in the construction of drones that could be used for surveillance in many circumstances, including military. Such research is still in its infancy.

Odonates in Research and Education

Odonates are excellent animals for testing theories in ecology, evolutionary biology, and conservation biology. Research takes many forms, and scientists who study these insects can spend long summer days at the shore of a lake or stream observing behavior, while their colleagues are macerating muscle tissue from an odonate leg to extract DNA from it to answer a question about the evolutionary relationships of species. It must be made clear that our first knowledge of Odonata came from museum collections, and they still represent a very important resource to continue growing that knowledge. Well-preserved specimens are always of value for taxonomic research and as vouchers for occurrence records, but they are of additional value to studies of phylogeny, morphology, migration, and other areas.

Perfect for field and laboratory research

Odonates lend themselves to field research, as they are large and diurnally active, most of them are identifiable in the field, and they congregate at the water to breed. So there are often large populations to be studied, and marked adults can be easy to monitor. Odonate behavior, including their daily schedule, mating behavior, and length of life, has been studied in quite a few species by capturing and marking individuals so they can be recognized from then on. They are usually marked on the wings: this used to be with colored paint spots that had to be deciphered with a code, but more recently, with better marking equipment, each one can receive an inked number. With binoculars they can be recorded at a distance, although damselflies may have

to be captured for their number to be read. The largest dragonflies can now be fitted with tiny transmitters that can be detected at greater distances.

Odonates can be monitored using adults, exuviae, or larvae. Each has its own advantages and disadvantages, but when done together they furnish exceptional information about population sizes, seasonality, and ecological and behavioral parameters.

Larvae are easy to collect in large numbers and keep in captivity for research of many sorts. They can be kept in controlled environments, so the effects of day length and water temperature on growth rate and timing can be worked out. They can also be fed different organisms in different amounts to see the effects of those experiments on the same variables. We still have relatively few species that have been reared from egg to adult, but eggs are not difficult to find, either by capturing exophytically ovipositing females and letting them lay their eggs into a container of pond water or watching for endophytically ovipositing species and gathering some of their eggs in plant tissue. This is not a task to be undertaken lightly, though, as it could involve many months of monitoring hatching and growth and providing food for hungry larvae the entire time.

After odonates emerge from the water, their exuviae are of great value to research. They can be collected every day from around ponds or along measured stretches of streams, for an almost complete census of the year's emergence, determining with perfect accuracy the abundance and seasonality of each species. Furthermore, DNA can be extracted from exuviae for identification and research into population genetics and phylogeny. The only caveat is that some exuviae, although easily placed in a genus, may be identified to species only with difficulty, as the species within a genus are often quite similar.

To understand this identification difficulty, we must note that the larva does not need to be recognizable for mating or territoriality, and their differences will be adaptations to their specific environment, perhaps minimal if they live together.

OPPOSITE: Dragonfly behavior is readily studied when they can be recognized as individuals, as in this *Cordulegaster sarracenia* in Texas marked with paint spots on the wings.

TOP: As electronics become ever more miniaturized, dragonflies can be tracked by tiny radio transmitters.

ABOVE: Much of what we know of the diversity of odonates comes from research collections all over the world.

Citizen science

Amateur naturalists play a great part in our learning about nature. In fact, they were the first to do so before there were academic biology departments. Citizen science, which uses these amateurs, has become more and more important in our society, as sheer numbers of people can contribute mountains of data to any study that can organize them. Nowadays thousands of people are excited about having their observations and photos of animals and plants in nature recorded in massive online databases with user-friendly interfaces. Portable devices such as cell phones are now routinely used as data-entry points.

Odonata Central

Odonata Central was established in 2004 to serve as a clearing house for records of the dragonflies and damselflies of the Americas. It began with a very large database of county records from the Lower 48 United States as well as latilong blocks in Canada and Alaska, based on published records and specimens in numerous

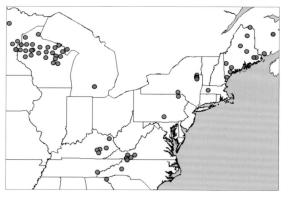

TOP: Dragonflies make excellent subjects for entomological education, as they are large, colorful, and active. Here a dragonfly class samples a pond.

ABOVE: Odonata Central gathers data on North American Odonata, producing distribution maps such as this for *Ophiogomphus howei.*

OPPOSITE: Studies of *Anax junius* have led to better understanding of migration.

collections. Those records were compiled over a period of years and published as a series of dot maps in 2004 —the first maps ever of all North American odonate species—and then incorporated into the Odonata Central database, which was then able to generate online maps.

The community of odonate enthusiasts was asked to continue to augment these maps by providing new photo and specimen records. The project has been a tremendous success, with close to a half million records in the constantly growing database that produces more and more accurate maps. As all records since 2004 are dated, they will be of value in defining flight seasons as well. Furthermore, they should prove valuable over time in determining the effects of climate change. Odonata Central data were used in the construction of the Dragonfly and Damselfly Field Guide and ID App for iOS devices (Birds in the Hand, LLC) that will be of service to all the citizen scientists in North America who made it possible.

All over the world now there are additional citizen-science websites for reporting natural-history observations (see Further Resources). As odonates are popular subjects for amateur naturalists and nature photographers, they are well represented in these programs. For example, almost two million verified odonate observations accompanied by photos have been submitted to Observation.org, a Dutch program, covering a substantial part of the globe.

Migratory Dragonfly Partnership

The Migratory Dragonfly Partnership was formed in 2010 to link observers in Canada, the United States, and Mexico, to further our understanding of long-distance dragonfly migration. The project has focused on just a few species, including the Common Green Darner (*Anax junius*) and Variegated Meadowhawk (*Sympetrum corruptum*), and through the input of observers all across the North American continent our knowledge of this phenomenon has advanced greatly. Even yearly variation can be noted.

Dragonflies and damselflies make good subjects for teachers. The enthralling behavior of adults can be watched throughout the summer in the temperate zone, and throughout the year at lower latitudes. The larvae can be easily raised in captivity, with lessons in camouflage, locomotion, predation, and, finally, metamorphosis and eclosion. The biggest concern in a community tank is keeping them from eating each other! In Japan special ponds have been constructed in the grounds of many schools so that students can enjoy and learn about odonates. Class projects are set up to monitor the species. I know of no other animals that are especially encouraged to come to school.

Anyone with sufficient space can dig a pond on their own property, and it is almost a guarantee that odonates will appear, sometimes surprisingly quickly.

Threats and Conservation

Environmental threats to odonates are of the sort that the natural world has been facing ever since human populations became large enough to have substantial effects on it. Among them are habitat loss, pollution, and the introduction of non-native species. Habitat loss is the primary extirpator of plant and animal populations, which cannot compress their natural density to accommodate ever-shrinking natural landscapes. Some species adapt to human populations better than others, and a few odonates are among them, flourishing in urban and suburban constructed wetlands, flooded rice fields, and canals and ditches.

Chemical pollution comes from polluting industries that flush their effluents into the nearest lake or, more likely, river. Rivers carry away toxic chemicals to the detriment of downstream plants and animals. Mining can cause severe pollution, and in mining regions around the world rivers may become virtually lifeless, neither invertebrates nor vertebrates being able to tolerate metal poisoning and extreme acidification of the water, much less the silt deposited by mining processes.

Insecticides, as their name implies, are surely another major threat to odonates. They have a great impact not only on the insects targeted, such as agricultural pests and disease carriers, but also on all the other species around them. Odonates are no exception to this; there is no program to eliminate dragonflies, but spraying to control mosquitoes and using a mixture of pesticides to protect farm crops will do so anyway. Even biological controls such as *Bacillus thuringiensis,* which is used against mosquitoes, will kill odonates. Recent studies found pesticide-contaminated streams to have 42 percent fewer freshwater invertebrates in Europe and 27 percent fewer in Australia in comparison with uncontaminated streams.

TOP: Dams like this one in Tasmania are harmful to most riverine animals, including odonates, because they change the nature of the river both above and below them.

ABOVE: Agriculture, here pineapple fields in Costa Rica, is essential to human survival but harmful to almost all other biota due to habitat destruction and pesticide use.

Dams also contribute to odonate mortality by changing the nature of rivers, with lotic habitats changed to lentic habitats above a dam and currents increasing below it. Canalization of a river goes further in changing the nature of the entire system. With slower current, less oxygen, and increased silt, most river species will decline. Groups with burrowing larvae such as clubtails (Gomphidae) will be especially affected. Finally, eutrophication, the nutrient overload that takes place in fresh water with the widespread application of fertilizers, as well as sewage and manure, changes habitats rapidly and can cause severe oxygen depletion.

Odonates for sale

It is shocking to search the internet for information about a large, showy insect and find only websites that offer it for sale. Some of these "collector's insects" can be raised in captivity, but many of them are taken from the wild and their existence threatened just to satisfy the desires of hobbyists. Fortunately, most Odonata do not preserve well as specimens, losing much of the color that makes them so attractive in life, especially their brilliant eye colors. Therefore they have not suffered the fate of overcollecting that has affected other groups, especially butterflies and beetles. Nevertheless, odonate species with brilliantly colored wings, as in the genera *Calopteryx*, *Neurobasis*, *Euphaea*, and *Celithemis*, are commonly listed for sale.

Climate change

Climate change is a new and pervasive threat to odonate populations. Global warming itself probably favors odonates, as they can spread to and survive at higher latitudes. Migrant dragonflies especially should be able to arrive earlier and go farther in spring, but residents will be favored as well. The many potential negative effects are poorly understood, but temperature is so important in the lives of odonates that there will undoubtedly be effects. For example, temperature affects seasonal regulation, phenology, and speed of development, as well as immune function. A more easily understood variable that comes along with higher temperatures is drought, and prolonged drought anywhere in the world will extirpate entire communities of odonates, at least locally.

Conservation status of world Odonata

Like all living organisms, odonates are involved in the "sixth great extinction" caused by human activities that is presently underway on the Earth. However, unlike vertebrate groups, in which relatively recent extinction has been documented for many species, it is often difficult to determine when an insect goes extinct. In the Odonata, there are only two known recent extinctions: the Saint Helena Darter (*Sympetrum dilatatum*) and the Maui Upland Damselfly (*Megalagrion jugorum*). Both of them lived on small islands, so they were at risk just because of their small range, and we can be certain of their extinction for the same reason. Two other Hawaiian *Megalagrion* damselflies have not been seen for more than sixty years and are probably extinct. In addition, it is extremely likely that many tropical-forest species with restricted ranges have gone extinct before being discovered.

In an extensive study for the International Union for the Conservation of Nature (IUCN) of about one-quarter of the world's Odonata species, published in 2009, it was discovered that odonates were generally in better shape than vertebrate groups. Almost one-third of those species had been assessed for their conservation status in the IUCN Red List, and about 15 percent of them were considered threatened with extinction (characterized as Threatened, Endangered, or Critically Endangered). This is a favorable proportion compared with an estimate of 29 percent for all animals that had been assessed for the Red List at that time. But of course 15 percent is too much. This relatively low figure is in part because odonates are accomplished dispersers, so they can colonize new areas and thus not be extirpated by the disappearance of individual wetlands.

Construction of artificial wetlands

On the positive side, the artificial wetlands we construct everywhere in the world can be of great value to Odonata. As they are good fliers and rapid colonizers, dragonflies appear at such wetlands as soon as they are created. A pair of Cardinal Meadowhawks (*Sympetrum*

TOP: *Megalagrion oresitrophum*, found only on Kauai, is one of 26 species of this genus that have evolved in the Hawaiian Islands. Three are now extinct.

ABOVE: *Megalagrion vagabundum* also occurs only on Kauai, but it has adapted to widespread human-caused ecosystem changes and is still common and widespread there.

illotum) began to oviposit in a pond we had just dug in our yard in Seattle as it was being filled with water, and their larvae developed and emerged. Artificial wetlands newly constructed in a Seattle park in 2010 had 17 species breeding in them in their first summer after construction, growing to 21 species after seven years. As was considered likely, increases in predatory birds and fish eliminated many individuals and perhaps even a few species by 2017, but large populations of Odonata nevertheless persisted in this section of the city where none previously were present.

LEFT: This pond in California was constructed largely with odonates in mind. In two decades 29 species have visited it and 19 of them successfully bred.

BELOW: There is still much to be discovered about dragonflies. This beautiful *Perithemis* is locally common in Costa Rica but is still undescribed to science.

Similar findings have been reported in studies in Europe, where even rare and declining species have found sanctuary in urban wetlands. Many studies of behavior and ecology have been carried out at these wetlands, and most importantly, they furnish sites for education of urban dwellers about Odonata and wetland ecology and conservation.

Ecosystem services

An oft-considered justification for biodiversity preservation is the value of other species to our own. For example, bees pollinate many of our crop plants. These species are said to be providing ecosystem services, but dragonflies are seldom mentioned in this context except for the potential of mosquito control by odonate larvae. Such potential has been established in experiments but has not been practical, as pest mosquitoes very often breed in habitats inaccessible to dragonflies.

Preserve wetlands, conserve odonates

Odonates are of great importance as indicators of habitat quality in wetlands, as adults are so easily

monitored. This has put them front and center in conservation biology. Nature preserves, some of them quite large and some with artificial wetlands, have been set aside specifically for dragonfly conservation in Brazil, England, Finland, Japan, and The Netherlands. The conservation of odonates depends on the preservation of aquatic habitats, and the entire diversity of these habitats, from tiny pools to large rivers in every country and every biome, must be included in this endeavor.

Desert Shadowdamsel
Palaemnema domina

Shadowdamsels, as their name implies, are damselflies of the shadows. The adults perch low in the forest understory and capture small insects there. They live in such dense vegetation that collectors and photographers have to crawl on hands and knees to find them, and capturing one with fingers is often easier than with an insect net. These forest lovers are among the most vulnerable odonates to extinction, as they occur in small, often isolated, populations that cannot persist when the trees that shelter them are cut down. And there are at least a few undescribed species in Central America, all with very restricted ranges.

The 43 species of shadowdamsels are often found in dense but very localized groups. The Desert Shadowdamsel, the northernmost species, perches in the tangles of exposed cottonwood roots along desert streams, and even if this exact microhabitat is rare, it is the only place it can be found. Males of the Presidio Shadowdamsel (*Palaemnema desiderata*) gather at certain waterside trees very early in the morning and mate with females that arrive; mating declines rapidly in mid-morning, which is unusual in odonates. Females oviposit in woody tissue over the water, with a male perched in attendance defending them from other males. This noncontact guarding by the male also is unusual among damselflies, although it is found as well in jewelwings and their relatives.

The larvae are among the most distinctive of damselflies, with heads shaped like those of termites and inflated caudal gills. The prementum of the labium is narrower in front and with relatively small palps, indicating quite small prey. The prementum has scales and ridges on it that are unusual among odonates and, like similar backward-pointing structures in the bills of birds, are presumed to prevent prey from escaping once captured. The type of prey remains unknown, like many things about the biology of these elusive odonates.

FAMILY	Platystictidae
DISTRIBUTION	Southern Arizona south through Mexico and Central America to Nicaragua
HABITAT	Shaded streams in forested or open country

1⁹⁄₁₆ in

4 cm

ABOVE: Shadowdamsels are typical of the tropics, but this species has extended its range up river drainages to southern Arizona.

Dancing Jewel
Platycypha caligata

The Dancing Jewel is a widely distributed and common damselfly that has been observed with great interest by researchers and dragonfly lovers alike. Males perch on rocks or stranded branches in their river habitat and defend a territory near an appropriate oviposition site for the species while waiting for females to arrive at the water. They drive other males away from this territory by flights that include flashing the white and red surfaces of their laterally expanded tibiae. There is no emergent vegetation in these rocky streams, so males have only scattered patches of acceptable substrates, making their territories discrete and defensible and the males very competitive.

When a female shows up, the male intercepts her and displays his blue abdomen, attracting her to an oviposition site with driftwood and/or tree roots. She lands and pauses if it does indeed seem appropriate. Meanwhile, he courts her by flying in an arc in front of her, facing her and presenting the anterior surfaces of his tibiae that produce a white blur in front of her. If she accepts the site, probably after testing the softness of the plant substrate, they copulate, then soon return to the site in tandem. The female then oviposits without the male, but she is likely to be joined by other females, until they aggregate in some numbers.

To explain the tibial colors, it has been speculated that red ("danger") should repel males while white ("peace") should attract females. Interestingly, one researcher caught males and altered their tibiae by painting them entirely or partially black, but they still were accepted by females as often as the unaltered control males. The tibiae are apparently more important in territorial interactions than in courtship, yet they are used in both ways. Nature is full of such mysteries, and each answer leads to new questions.

FAMILY	Chlorocyphidae
DISTRIBUTION	Widespread in sub-Saharan Africa
HABITAT	Wooded streams and rivers

1¼ in
3.2 cm

ABOVE & LEFT: Jewels show the sexual dimorphism that is so common in odonates, the male bright for display (left) and the female (above) camouflaged for bouts of oviposition at the stream surface. Chlorocyphids are odd damselflies, the only ones with abdomens shorter than their wings, perhaps an adaptation to make their flight less stable during dancing courtship flights.

Great Cascade Damsel
Thaumatoneura inopinata

This large damselfly is one of the "holy grails" of odonate seekers in Costa Rica and Panama. Never common, it has become less so with forest destruction. It breeds only at waterfalls, where males hang from the vegetation and fly back and forth along the face of the waterfall, even in its spray, so that water droplets collect on them.

The clear-winged and black-winged male forms were originally thought to be two different species, but it was soon realized that they were the same. The females, clear-winged but with black wingtips, were also found to be the same species when observed closely almost a century ago. Later studies on other kinds of damselflies showed a similar male polymorphism that is probably paralleled by a polymorphism in behavior. Although this has not been documented for *Thaumatoneura*, we have some understanding of this phenomenon in the closely related *Paraphlebia* of Mexico and upper Central America.

In two species of *Paraphlebia*, most males with black wingtips hold territories, court females and mate with them. Other males in the same population are clear-winged, and most of them are probably behaving as "sneakers" or "floaters"—individuals that do not defend territories but instead move up and down a forest stream attempting to mate with females that have been attracted to the territories of territorial males. They are usually less successful than the black-winged males.

Thaumatoneura females lay their eggs in beds of wet moss, and the larvae crawl around in these beds and on the rock faces. When they transform into an adult, the wings are at first bright green, resembling the leaves of small herbaceous plants growing on the rocks. The green color comes from the damselfly's hemolymph, but perhaps it persists in the wings as a form of camouflage until the adult is ready to fly away.

FAMILY	Thaumatoneuridae
DISTRIBUTION	Costa Rica and western Panama
HABITAT	Waterfalls in primary forest

2¾ in
7 cm

RIGHT: **This very large species, here a female, is impressive enough to be a destination in its own right for Costa Rican ecotourists with odonate interests.**

Aurora Bluetail
Ischnura aurora

This tiny damselfly is a remarkable traveler. No other zygopteran has such a large range in Asia/Australasia, and it is also widely distributed across the Pacific islands. Our best example of wind dispersal in odonates, it has even been found at desert waterholes far from other wetlands. In an event rare or absent in other odonates, the females mate only while immature, in fact usually while still teneral, as has been noted in Australia and New Zealand. In those countries, mature females persistently reject any attempt at mating.

Upon insemination, the female disperses away from the wetland from which she emerged, and that dispersal may be to a great distance, as she rises into the air and is taken by prevailing winds. As she matures, she begins to produce eggs that can be fertilized by the sperm stored in her reproductive tract, and she can colonize temporary pools and other just-formed wetlands, including new locations for the species. Probably many females are lost at sea, but others extend the range of the species until there is no more land. Larval development takes 8–10 weeks, allowing frequent colonization events over the course of a tropical year.

Interestingly, mating with teneral females has not been observed on the Asian mainland. Instead, females there mate when sexually mature, often with more than one male, and sperm displacement occurs as in most damselflies. They then form resident populations in permanent waters, mated females not ascending to the sky to be blown away. This probably explains the much sparser occurrence of *I. aurora* across southeastern Asia, where the larvae of many other coenagrionids may be superior competitors in permanent wetlands. We still know very little about competition in damselfly larvae.

FAMILY	Coenagrionidae
DISTRIBUTION	Southern Asia from Pakistan east to Japan and China (but not ubiquitous in the Indo-Malayan region), Philippines, the Lesser Sunda Islands, New Guinea, and Australia; widespread on Pacific islands east to the Marshall Islands, French Polynesia, and New Zealand
HABITAT	Ponds, lakes, and marshes of all kinds, including rice fields and mangrove swamps

⅞ in
2.2 cm

RIGHT: **This tiny damselfly is the only odonate in which males breed with just-emerged females, which then are taken by prevailing winds to colonize new territory.**

Four-spot Midget
Mortonagrion hirosei

This small damselfly has been found in scattered populations along the coasts of Japan as well as farther south on the edge of the Pacific. Because of its rarity, it has been better studied than some common species and has received enough notoriety to be featured on a Hong Kong postage stamp. It can be common, but its habitat is localized and subject to dredging and filling. The adults live for about 35 days but are weak fliers and remain in the dense vegetation of their habitat. One study found that immatures changed perches about 120 times and moved an average of only 30 ft (9 m) in a day. Mature adults flew twice as often and moved three times as far.

Dragonflies and damselflies have been much considered for biological control of harmful insects, but as generalized predators they are of less value than species that prey on or parasitize the target insects. As the target species declines, odonates will turn to other prey, releasing the intended prey from predator pressure. However, laboratory tests indicate their potential value, and larval odonates have been used to control pests in Asian rice paddies and disease-carrying mosquitoes in household water cisterns in Myanmar.

Furthermore, this species is one in which using adult odonates has been considered. Sandflies (no-see-ums) of the family Ceratopogonidae are extremely bothersome to human populations, coming out at dusk from salt marshes and mangrove swamps and exhibiting a biting fierceness out of all proportion to their size. But they are exactly the prey that make up much of the diet of *M. hirosei*. The thought was that placing this species elsewhere in the world in brackish marshes would not only reduce sandfly numbers but also improve the survival prospects of this rare damselfly. Some local transplantation has been successful in Japan.

FAMILY	Coenagrionidae
DISTRIBUTION	Coastal regions of eastern Honshu, Hong Kong, and Taiwan
HABITAT	Fresh and brackish coastal marshes and streams

1¼ in
3.1 cm

RIGHT: On a warm, sunny afternoon at a wetland, damselflies in copulation are usually easy to find. Notice both sexes can hold on to the perch.

Green Hawker
Aeshna viridis

This large dragonfly is quite unusual in its dependence on a single plant species as larval habitat, at least in parts of its range. This plant is Water Soldier (*Stratiotes aloides*). An odd-looking plant with a rosette of serrated leaves and large white flowers, its distinctiveness facilitates searching for Green Hawkers. The plant is declining in parts of its European range but, because it is a commercial nursery plant, it has been introduced into still other regions, with potential for colonization by *A. viridis*. The distinctiveness of the plant renders it not only easily noted by plant enthusiasts but also by wandering dragonflies, large dragonflies having very high dispersal potential.

Female Green Hawkers are the greenest of the genus and are well camouflaged when roosting low in herbaceous vegetation, which they prefer over woodland. Where they are dependent on a single host plant for the larva, they are generally less common and with a patchier distribution than most of their near relatives. But because they depend on a single plant species, it is easier to find populations of *A. viridis* in a complex landscape.

Mating takes place in early morning, even before sunrise. Males fly into dense stands of grasses and rushes looking for roosting females. Usually they do not bother the ones with wings severely frayed from the sharp teeth of the *Stratiotes*; perhaps those females are less likely to continue ovipositing. The eggs are laid only in living plant tissue and only beneath the water surface, typically 20–40 eggs in a clump in each leaf. This is distinctly different from the orderly lines of eggs typical of other members of their family that usually oviposit in plant tissue above the water. The eggs overwinter and hatch early in the next spring, and the larva takes two years to reach emergence.

FAMILY	Aeshnidae
DISTRIBUTION	Northern Europe from The Netherlands to western Siberia
HABITAT	Lakes, ponds, marshes, and ditches with its host plant

2⁹⁄₁₆ in
6.5 cm

LEFT: Male Green Hawkers fly patterns over freshwater marshes attempting to find willing mates.

BELOW LEFT: The females, camouflaged to us, are presumably easier for them to detect.

Black-tailed Ringtail
Erpetogomphus molossus

One of the most exciting experiences for a field biologist is to discover a new species. The Black-tailed Ringtail was discovered on a September 2004 expedition to the montane Sierra Madre Occidental of the northern state of Sonora in Mexico. The area where it occurs is covered by pine–oak forest in very good condition, with shallow streams running through it at intervals and an abundance of wildflowers in the autumn. While surveying the area southeast of Yécora on a sunny afternoon, we stopped at a particularly nice-looking stream at 4,454 ft (1,385 m) elevation.

One of the first dragonflies that caught our attention was a beautiful clubtail with blue eyes, bright green thorax, and black, white, and brown abdomen. Males were perched on rocks in the stream, and similarly colored females were in shrubs in open meadows nearby. We knew it was in the genus *Erpetogomphus*, but we knew in addition that we had never seen this species before. Without our libraries, perusal of the literature was not possible, but a quick check on a laptop computer at the dinner table revealed that it was none of the known species.

Three members of the crew, working on a book on the Odonata of the region, took it on themselves to describe the species, and after the usual time spent examining specimens and designating one of them as a type specimen (holotype), they proceeded to describe, measure, and illustrate it meticulously and submit a manuscript for publication in the prestigious journal *Zootaxa*. The new species was brought forth to the world in November 2013. In the spirit of naming ringtails after snakes, the species name comes from the Black-tailed Rattlesnake (*Crotalus molossus*)—a species of the same region.

FAMILY	Gomphidae
DISTRIBUTION	Mountains of eastern Sonora, Mexico
HABITAT	Forested montane streams

1⅞ in
4.8 cm

ABOVE & LEFT: This striking clubtail species (male above) remained unknown until discovered on an expedition to northern Mexico in 2004. It was then formally described in 2013.

Hine's Emerald
Somatochlora hineana

Hine's Emerald has the distinction of being the only North American odonate listed as Endangered under the US Endangered Species Act. One advantage of being so listed is that funds become available for research, and this dragonfly has now been studied more than most other odonates on the continent. As a result, new populations have been discovered, and we know more about its basic biology than we do about many other common odonates. From all the new information, we also know that it is more secure than several other North American species of much more restricted range, such as the San Francisco Forktail (*Ischnura gemina*) and Tennessee Clubtail (*Gomphus sandrius*).

Females lay more than 500 eggs during their life, and the larvae spend two to four years in the water. Larvae may shelter in burrows of a crayfish (*Cambarus diogenes*) during low temperatures or drought conditions. The crayfish eat the larvae, but the burrows are essential to the species. This is not a rare dragonfly in optimal habitat; numbers have been estimated in the thousands at two of the best-known Wisconsin sites. Nevertheless, populations in different states are isolated by distance, and Illinois populations are distinct genetically from those in Wisconsin and Michigan.

The adults patrol widely after flying insects, and while doing so the most obvious cause of mortality is being hit by fast-moving vehicles, both automobiles and trains; many are found dead at the roadside. Appropriate habitat for this species on dolomite bedrock has always been scattered, and it has been destroyed or fragmented in many parts of the emerald's range. Industrial, agricultural, and urban development have all played a part, as have logging, off-road vehicle use, creation of water impoundments, and building of roads and pipelines. Off-site hydrology alterations have affected the groundwater-fed seeps and springs that support Hine's Emerald wetland habitats.

FAMILY	Corduliidae
DISTRIBUTION	Southern Ontario and Michigan southwest to Missouri; formerly in Indiana, Ohio, and Alabama
HABITAT	Calcareous fens, sedge meadows with slowly flowing water, and streamlets within cattail marshes

2⅜ in
6.1 cm

ABOVE & LEFT: Hine's Emerald (female above) was thought to be very rare, even listed as endangered, until research funds were made available to broaden the search for it.

Broad-bodied Chaser
Libellula depressa

Both common and scientific names are appropriate, as this species probably has the widest, flattest abdomen for its length of any odonate. There are several possible advantages of a broad abdomen. First, for a species that flies early in spring, a broad abdomen warms up faster in the sun than a narrow abdomen would. Second, for a species that displays its abdomen in territorial squabbles, greater breadth means a more prominent display. Many adaptations are multipurpose.

Broad-bodied Chasers are familiar dragonflies in much of Europe, as they are among the first species to colonize newly constructed wetlands, as in city parks and wildlife sanctuaries. They prefer smaller water bodies and can appear at garden ponds, as long as they are not densely vegetated. They are also known to spend time over the shiny surfaces of automobiles, a behavior reported in many odonate species, treating them quite erroneously as small ponds. Dragonflies are creatures of instinct, not careful deliberation.

After arriving at a wetland, males do not defend fixed territories. They alternate perching with extensive flights, usually covering the entire perimeter of the water body. They display at each other during these flights, flying in parallel with that broad abdomen strikingly conspicuous. When a female is encountered, the male grabs her and in the air performs a very brief sperm translocation, then an almost equally brief copulation that averages about eight seconds. The female then begins to oviposit somewhere in the near vicinity.

The male remains in a noncontact guarding position near the female as she oviposits. Fierce chases of intruding males may compromise the guarding, and the first male may lose his mate to another. But then likely he will mate again and accompany the new female to a different oviposition site.

FAMILY	Libellulidae
DISTRIBUTION	Throughout much of Europe east to western Russia, Turkmenistan and Afghanistan
HABITAT	Open ponds and small lakes

1¾ in
4.5 cm

ABOVE & LEFT: Sexual dimorphism can be produced by pruinosity, the secretion of a waxy substance that colors a brown immature abdomen (above) pale blue in a mature male (left).

Eastern Amberwing
Perithemis tenera

Amberwings are the smallest dragonflies at the lakes and ponds where they occur, but they make up in activity what they lack in size. Males are aggressively territorial, and each one establishes a territory around a potential oviposition site that should be attractive to females. A pond full of amberwings involves constant motion, with males flying over the open water and engaging in constant standoffs that involve fluttering their golden-orange wings while hovering and facing one another.

A male examines a potential site closely, this usually being a patch of floating vegetation or even cups in water-lily leaves. Could he be checking for predators? When a female approaches his territory, the male follows her while swaying from side to side, then turns and flies slowly to the chosen site and hovers over it. If the female is interested, she flies slowly and perches nearby. The male then grabs her and copulation ensues. This lasts no more than 15–20 seconds, apparently allowing both sperm displacement and insemination to take place.

After separation, the male flies slowly back to the oviposition site with the female following close behind. He hovers over the site until she begins to oviposit, then flies around her, repelling any male that approaches. The presence of the male is important to the female, as it indicates the site is predator-free. She lays all her eggs at the site, and they "explode" as they hit the water, scattering in a way that reduces their density and hence gives each egg access to precious oxygen.

A thorough study of this species published in 1955 was among the first to show the complexity of behavior in adult dragonflies. Among other things, it showed that the quality of the oviposition site was more important than any feature of the male other than his ability to defend that territory.

FAMILY	Libellulidae
DISTRIBUTION	Throughout eastern North America, southwest to northern Mexico
HABITAT	Lakes, ponds, and slow streams with open water

⅞ in
2.3 cm

ABOVE & LEFT: As in many species, interactions between male (left) and female Eastern Amberwings leading to reproduction are facilitated by the strong color dimorphism in both body and wings.

Amazon Sapphirewing
Zenithoptera fasciata

So many odonates are surprising when first seen, and this is a good example. A male of this small dragonfly species may be spotted by its bright blue wings shining in the sun, and then suddenly it closes them, showing nothing but black undersides and virtually disappearing when viewed from above. Four species of sapphirewings live in still waters in Central and South America, all being similar in these ways. Both the blue upper wings, flashing like those of a *Morpho* butterfly, and the ability to close them at will are unique in the skimmer family. Superficially similar are small libellulids of the genus *Diastatops* with black wings, some of them having bright red patches at the base. *Diastatops* can move all four wings independently to display their shiny upper sides in various ways, but they cannot close them.

The blue wing coloration of *Zenithoptera* comes from a complex set of layers in the wing membrane: alternating layers of melanized and unmelanized cuticle and diffuse scattering of two different layers of wax crystals on the upper surface. There are tiny respiratory channels in these wings, so they are alive—the only odonates in which this has been suggested.

When not at the water, sapphirewings roost at the tips of twigs with their wings in either of their two positions. When the wings are drooped, the dragonfly looks like a little parasol from the side or below, and they can be spotted like that well up into the canopy, flying out after insects. Many dragonflies of the rain forest go up into the canopy to feed, this region having more sunshine and more insect life than the understory. We know almost nothing about which species go up there, however. Odonatologists have not yet taken advantage of the many opportunities for canopy access in tropical forests.

FAMILY	Libellulidae
DISTRIBUTION	Nicaragua to southern Peru and northern Brazil
HABITAT	Rain-forest ponds and swamps

1 in
2.5 cm

ABOVE: This female sapphirewing at a forest trail has closed her wings to become less conspicuous, even hiding the abdomen to look nothing like a dragonfly.

LEFT: Sapphirewings are unique dragonflies, both from the color of their wings (here a male) and from their ability to show or hide their distinctive coloration.

CHAPTER SIX
Odonate Diversity Around the World

The evolutionary tree of odonates is becoming clearer from recent genetic studies. Within the common odonate form, there is a great diversity in size, shape, color, and behavior among the 39 living families. Diversity ranges from three very successful families that together include more than half of the odonate species to four relict families with only a single species each.

Species Diversity

How many species?

In 2003, the total number of Odonata species was estimated at about 5,500. By September 2018, there were 6,299 described modern odonate species: 3,192 Zygoptera, 3 Anisozygoptera, and 3,104 Anisoptera. Of that number, 121 new species were described from the world tropics just in 2016 and 2017. Sixty were described from Africa in a single paper in 2015. Our knowledge of the diversity of the group is increasing so rapidly that it is obvious we still have much to learn! A 2008 paper estimated there may be 7,000 living species.

A very widespread group

Odonates occur on all continents except Antarctica. They thrive where there are high temperatures, so they are few in the Arctic. Nevertheless, a few species occur north to just above the Arctic Circle in both North America and Eurasia, including the Sedge Darner/Moorland Hawker (*Aeshna juncea*). With decreasing latitude, diversity goes up rapidly, and there is substantial odonate diversity as far north as southern Canada, Germany, and northern Japan, and as far south as Chile, South Africa, and southern Australia.

Tropical diversity

As in most organisms, the highest diversity of Odonata is found in the tropics, where there is a steady turnover as well as an increase in species. Rather few localities from all around the world have been sufficiently surveyed that their species lists can be compared, but the lists with the greatest numbers of species are from tropical areas (see Table opposite). The highest number at a single site is the 187 species recorded at Explorer's Inn in southern Peru, where a great diversity of habitats supports a great diversity of species.

TOP: This *Argia chelata* pair represents the most diverse odonate genus in the New World. A stream in Mexico or Central America may have a dozen *Argia* species.

ABOVE: *Pseudagrion* is the largest odonate genus, found throughout the Old World tropics and especially diverse in Africa. This male *Pseudagrion dispar* is typical.

The order Odonata is an old group, with some worldwide families. They may have occurred widely on the northern and southern megacontinents, Laurasia and Gondwana, of 150 million years ago. They would then have traveled with those land masses as they separated so very slowly into the continents we know today. Alternatively, the families are widespread because odonates are such good dispersers. Groups with the most widespread species—the pond damsels (Coenagrionidae), darners (Aeshnidae), and skimmers (Libellulidae)—are still moving between continents.

Continental and island diversities

Diversity is quite high throughout eastern North America and eastern Asia, but less so in western North America and Europe. As glaciers spread, many of the organisms they pushed southward were able to survive as habitats remained suitable and then return northward as the glaciers retreated. But in Europe, the Mediterranean Sea and the deserts of North Africa were barriers to the dispersal of freshwater animals such as odonates, as apparently were arid regions of western North America.

African odonates are loosely divided into two groups—savanna species and forest species. Many of the savanna species occur almost continent-wide south of the Sahara. The forest-based species are more diverse but more local, some of them extremely so, as forest dwellers are limited by open regions. In the Cape Region of far southern Africa there are numerous endemic odonates, which are presumed relicts of a south-temperate fauna once more widespread.

South America is wetter than Africa, with a large proportion of species forest-adapted, but there are still many species of open wetlands inhabiting the Orinoco Llanos of the north and the Patagonian pampas of the south. And, even more so than in Africa, there is an ancient southern element in the temperate forests of the southern Andes.

Because of its long isolation, Australia has a large fauna of endemic species, genera, and even families,

ABOVE: *Olpogastra lugubris*, a common species in many parts of Africa, possesses the most slender abdomen of any dragonfly.

BELOW: Odonata species totals from some well-studied neotropical sites. Larger numbers indicate larger areas or longer periods sampled.

COUNTRY	LOCALITY	SPECIES
Mexico	Turtle, Veracruz	133
Costa Rica	Hacienda Taboga	98
Costa Rica	La Selva	123
Costa Rica	Rincón de Osa	89
Panama	Barro Colorado Island	91
Ecuador	Limoncocha	149
Peru	Explorama Lodge	100
Peru	Pakitza	117
Peru	Explorer's Inn	187
Brazil	Iguazú	107

some of which extend into New Guinea and other islands to the north, where they meet the large fauna of southern Asia inhabiting the same islands. The best dispersers among these species have colonized the many island chains extending far out in the Pacific, all the way to Hawaii, where a few dozen species are endemic. The Galápagos Islands, 600 miles (1,000 km) west of South America, have been colonized entirely from that continent and have spawned only a single endemic species, *Rhionaeschna galapagoensis*.

Phylogeny

With so many species in such great variety in this group of insects, we are working diligently to try to fit all of them into a clear evolutionary pattern—a phylogenetic tree of odonates. Much of what we know about odonates is based on specimens, and museums around the world hold large collections of Odonata that are available for specimen-based research. The largest collections contain several hundred thousand specimens, allowing studies of the many kinds of variation acted on by natural selection: sexual, ontogenetic, seasonal, geographic, and individual.

The morphological basis of classification

Patterns of wing venation have long been used as a basic tool in odonate classification, but the realization has slowly come about that wings may become narrower or broader for ecological or behavioral reasons, and to do so they have to lose or add veins. This complicates the picture, especially because so much of the classification of fossil odonates has been based on wing venation.

The wings are mostly nonliving tissue and are not very edible to bacteria when an odonate at the end of its life settles to the bottom of a pond. Because they are flat, the wings do not become deformed like the body and head. Thus they may be the only parts well preserved as silt, little by little, covers their flat surfaces, the silt eventually turning into rock. So we have to treat our conclusions about the early evolution and diversity of the odonates with at least a bit of caution.

The new tool of genetics

Odonates of course have an abundance of morphological features besides wing venation that can be used to elucidate relationships, and even behavioral and ecological features add to our knowledge of the living species. To them must be added genetic studies, and those have been pursued with vigor just in the past few decades. Now we are establishing the phylogeny of the order Odonata as a continuing story. More and more species have been sampled for

LEFT: *Neocordulia batesi*, here a male in Panama, is one of the "emerald" dragonflies with no samples available for genetic study and a still-uncertain family placement.

BELOW: A phylogenetic tree shows the proposed relationships of the families of anisopteran dragonflies.

their DNA, more and more often with more than one gene being examined, and more and more papers are being published about the relationships indicated by the similarity of those genes. It won't be long before entire genomes are sampled from these primitive and important insects.

How do we get these genetic samples? We have to have tissue from an individual of the species to extract DNA from it. Fortunately, because of the polymerase chain reaction (PCR) developed in 1983, it is easy to get many strands of DNA from small samples, so a single leg can be taken from an odonate and used for multiple genetic studies. The individual can be released or, much better for science, retained as a voucher specimen so the genetic material can always be tied to a known individual.

From studies published as recently as 2015, we have a much better idea of the relationships among the families and which genera belong in which family than we did even a decade ago. But in both the Anisoptera and Zygoptera, there are still questions of phylogeny in

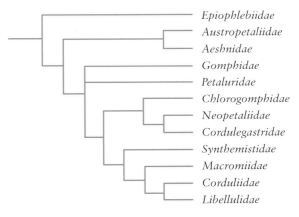

Epiophlebiidae
Austropetaliidae
Aeshnidae
Gomphidae
Petaluridae
Chlorogomphidae
Neopetaliidae
Cordulegastridae
Synthemistidae
Macromiidae
Corduliidae
Libellulidae

groups that have not been adequately sampled. A well-established phylogeny of Anisoptera is presented here, but numerous genera of Zygoptera don't fit in one of the established families, so a useful phylogeny of this suborder is still elusive. Much further study involving a greater variety of genes will be necessary before all the damselflies are placed where they belong on the Tree of Life.

The Families of Odonates

Zygoptera (damselflies)

Hemiphlebiidae **Greenling**

1 species in southern Australia.

Perilestidae **Twigtails**

19 species in 2 genera in Central and South America.

Synlestidae **Malachites**

38 species in 9 genera in Australia, southern Asia, and southern Africa, with single distant relicts in western Africa and Hispaniola.

Lestidae **Spreadwings**

153 species in 9 genera distributed worldwide.

There are 39 families of Odonata recognized in the present classification system, all listed below. Perhaps one of the most interesting aspects of the system is the number of families with one or a few species, almost surely indicating a group that was once more widespread and diverse and has little by little been whittled down to just a remnant of its former glory.

Calopterygidae **Jewelwings/Demoiselles**

182 species in 21 genera with worldwide distribution except for Australia.

Dicteriadidae **Barelegs**

2 species in 2 genera in tropical South America.

Polythoridae **Bannerwings**

59 species in 7 genera in Middle and South America.

Euphaeidae **Satinwings**

77 species in 9 genera in Asia, one of these species also occurring in eastern Europe.

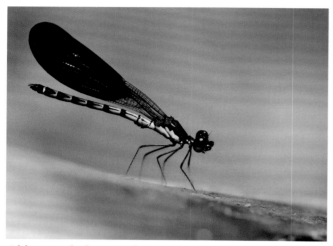

Chlorocyphidae **Jewels**

157 species in 20 genera in Africa, southern Asia, and Australasia.

Amphipterygidae **Mayan Damsels**

5 species in one genus in Mexico and Central America.

Rimanellidae **Tepui Damsel**

1 species in 1 genus in northern South America.

Pentaphlebiidae **Relic Damsels**

3 species in 1 genus in western Africa.

Devadattidae **Grisettes**

13 species in 1 genus in southeastern Asia and associated islands.

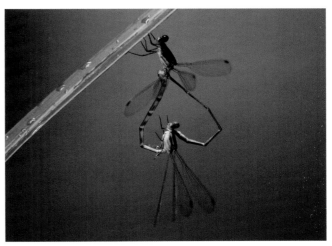

Heteragrionidae **Flamboyant Flatwings**

57 species in 2 genera from central Mexico to Argentina.

Hypolestidae **Caribbean Flatwings**

3 species in 1 genus in the Greater Antilles.

Megapodagrionidae **Long-legged Flatwings**

29 species in 3 genera in South America.

Philogeniidae **Dusky Flatwings**

42 species in 2 genera in Central and South America.

Thaumatoneuridae **Cascade Damsels**

5 species in 2 genera in Mexico and Central America.

Philogangidae **Titans**

4 species in 1 genus on the southern Asian mainland.

Philosinidae **Rainbow Flatwings**

12 species in 2 genera in southern Asia.

Pseudolestidae **Phoenix**

1 species in 1 genus on Hainan Island, China.

Lestoideidae **Bluestreaks and Rockmasters**

9 species in 2 genera in Australia.

Argiolestidae **Australasian Flatwings**

116 species in 20 genera in southern Asia and throughout Australasia, more isolated genera in Madagascar and western Africa.

Incertae Sedis

71 species in 14 genera in South America, East Africa and Madagascar, and eastern Asia, including the Sunda Islands, have not been placed in specific families because of a lack of genetic data.

Platystictidae **Shadowdamsels**

269 species in 10 genera in New World and Asian tropics;
most diverse in Asia.

Isostictidae **Narrow-wings**

47 species in 12 genera in Australasia.

Platycnemididae **Stream Damsels**

464 species in 42 genera in Europe, Asia, Australasia, and Africa.

Coenagrionidae **Pond Damsels**

1,354 species in 121 genera distributed worldwide.

Anisozygoptera

Epiophlebiidae **Damsel Dragons**

3 species in 1 genus in Japan, China, and the Himalayas.

Anisoptera (dragonflies)

Petaluridae **Petaltails**

11 species in 5 genera, occurring locally in moist, mostly temperate regions: northwestern and southeastern North America, southern South America, Japan, far eastern and southwestern Australia, and New Zealand.

Austropetaliidae **Redspots**

11 species in 4 genera in southern South America and southeastern Australia.

Neopetaliidae **Funneltail**

1 species in 1 genus in southern South America.

Aeshnidae **Darners/Hawkers**

480 species in 54 genera distributed worldwide.

Gomphidae **Clubtails**

1,015 species in 102 genera distributed worldwide.

Chlorogomphidae **Skydragons**

53 species in 3 genera in Asia.

Cordulegastridae **Spiketails/Goldenrings**

55 species in 3 genera in North and Middle America and Eurasia.

Macromiidae **Cruisers**

123 species in 4 genera in North America, Eurasia, Australia and Africa.

Synthemistidae **Tigertails**

150 species in 28 genera in Australasia, Asia, Madagascar, South Africa and South America; an isolated species in Europe.

Corduliidae **Emeralds**

165 species in 22 genera in the northern hemisphere, extending through tropical America and Australasia, with a single species in eastern Africa.

Libellulidae **Skimmers**

1,040 species in 140 genera distributed worldwide.

Glossary

Many of these terms are defined where first given in the text, but the glossary can be used for any additional reading about Odonata.

aestivation - dormancy/inactivity during the warm season

andromorph - female morph with male-like colors

anisopteran - member of suborder Anisoptera; dragonfly

anterior - front

anthropogenic - caused by humans

biliverdin - a bile pigment produced by the breakdown of hemoglobin

branchial basket - the complex of gills in the rectum of Anisoptera

bursa copulatrix - one of the sperm-storage organs of a female odonate

caudal - referring to the tail

cell - one of the sections of an odonate wing bounded by veins

cercus - paired appendage at end of abdomen in all odonates (pl. cerci)

chemoreceptor - a sensory receptor that detects chemicals, including odors

congeneric - of the same genus

conspecific - of the same species

counterstroke - alternate beating of forewings and hindwings

crepuscular - active at dusk and, often, dawn

cuticle - outer covering of Odonata and all other arthropods

diapause - period of dormancy caused by decreasing day length

diaphragm - band of tissue between thorax and abdomen

dorsal - upper surface

eclosion - visible transformation from larval to adult odonate

ecosystem services - direct and indirect contributions of ecosystems to human well-being

ectoparasite - a parasite on the outside of another animal's body

ectotherm - animal with body temperature regulated by environmental temperature

emergence - odonate larva leaving the water to molt into an adult

endophytic - "within plants"; refers to oviposition by Odonata that have an ovipositor and insert their eggs within plant tissues

endothermy - generation by animal of heat to regulate body temperature

epiphytic - "upon plants"; refers either to dragonflies that lay their eggs upon (not within) plants or to plants that grow on other plants (water held by these plants may serve as breeding habitats for odonates)

epiproct - lower terminal appendage in Anisoptera

euryhaline - occurs in both fresh and salt water

eutrophication - the enrichment of a water body with nutrients, usually in excess

exophytic - "outside plants"; refers to oviposition by Odonata that drop their eggs freely into water or in some cases on land that will be flooded

exuvia - cast skin of emerged odonate (pl. exuviae)

facultative - behavior at the discretion of an animal, not fixed

femur - basal leg segment (pl. femora)

fertilization pore - opening from bursa copulatrix to oviduct

flight season - the period during which adults of a species are on the wing

genital ligula - copulatory organ of male Zygoptera

genital pore - opening of male or female reproductive system; also gonopore

gill tuft - external tuft of gills at end of abdomen

gonopore - opening of male or female reproductive system; also genital pore

gynomorph - dull morph of polymorphic female odonate; also heteromorph

hamule - structure(s) on abdominal segment 2 of male odonate, shaped to hold female abdomen tightly during copulation; both anterior and posterior pairs

head-arrester system - sclerites that temporarily lock the odonate head to the thorax for stability

heliophile - sun lover

hemoglobin - oxygen-transporting protein in vertebrate blood

hemolymph - insect body fluid

heteromorph - dull morph of polymorphic female odonate; also gynomorph

hyaline - clear, pigmentless

imaginal disc - larval tissue remaining during metamorphosis that is the source of the developing adult

immature - in odonates, adult individual that has not reached sexual maturity

incertae sedis - taxonomic placement uncertain

inferior - lower in the context of odonate terminal appendages

insectivore - diet of insects

instar - stage in larval life; also stadium

keystone predator - a species that influences the species composition of a habitat and thus its very nature by selectively feeding on only certain types of prey

labial palp - structure articulated to labium to hold prey

labium - "lower lip" mouthpart

lamellae - plates, in the case of odonates referring to the caudal structures of damselflies

larva - growth stage of odonate, hatched from egg and developing into adult; also nymph, naiad

lateral - side

latilong blocks - rectangular geographic regions defined by latitude and longitude

lek - group of males displaying to attract females

lentic - still water

lotic - flowing/running water

maiden flight - first flight of a just-emerged odonate

melanized - made darker with dark melanin pigment

mesostigmal lamina - plate at front of thorax in female damselflies that engages paraprocts of male during copulation

metamorphosis - change, in odonates a dramatic change that occurs in the final larval stage to form the adult

naiad - nymph, larva

nodus - prominent crossvein at front of odonate wing

nymph - larva, naiad

obelisking - pointing abdomen upward to reduce sun rays falling on it

ocellus - one of three simple eyes on odonate head (pl. ocelli)

ommatidium - individual simple eye that with others makes up the compound eye of an insect (pl. ommatidia)

ontogenetic - age-related

opsin - protein that controls reception of particular color

oviduct - duct that carries eggs to be laid

oviposition - egg-laying

ovipositor - structure through which odonates lay eggs

paraproct - lower terminal appendage in Zygoptera, occurring in pairs

parthenogenesis - reproduction in which females produce all-female offspring, with no males and no sexual behavior

phoresy - a smaller animal using a large one to transport it from place to place

phytotelmata - above-ground plant "container" that holds water

polychromatism - occurring in more than one color

polymorphism - occurring in more than one shape; in odonates used as equivalent to polychromatism

posterior - rear

prementum - main part of labium

prolarva - first stage of larva hatching from egg, quite different from succeeding stages (pl. prolarvae)

pronymph - prolarva

prothorax - small, separate part of thorax with first pair of legs

pruinose, pruinosity - the deposit of a pale, waxy substance on the outside of the cuticle of an odonate and its effect on coloration

pseudopupil - dark spot(s) in odonate eyes that show ommatidia pointing toward observer

pterostigma - thickened cell on costa (the anteriormost wing vein) near wingtip; also stigma

pterothorax - large section of thorax with second and third pairs of legs and two pairs of wings

pupa - resting stage in which metamorphosis takes place in advanced insects

relict - restricted from a previously wider distribution

resilin - flexible protein at junctions of veins in the wing riffle - the flowing part of a stream between relatively still pools

sciophile - shade lover

sclerite - a small section of cuticle that is articulated with another section

seasonal regulation - larval development pattern that determines adult flight season

sensillum - tiny sensory structure on cuticle (pl. sensilla)

seta - bristle or spine (pl. setae)

siccatation - dormancy during dry season

spermatheca - paired female sperm-storage organ (pl. spermathecae)

sperm transfer/translocation - action of male transferring sperm from gonopore to copulatory organ

spiracle - respiratory opening in insect cuticle

spring species - a species that overwinters in the final larval instar and thus has a short spring flight season

stadium - stage in larval life; also instar (pl. stadia)

stylus - paired sensory structure on ovipositor (pl. styli)

subgenital plate - plate under female abdomen tip to hold eggs for laying; also vulvar lamina

superior - upper in the context of odonate terminal appendages

tandem - prolonged connection of male terminal appendages to female head or thorax

tarsal claw - paired structure at end of tarsus

tarsus - terminal segment of leg (pl. tarsi)

teneral - just-emerged individual, soft and colorless

tibia - second segment of leg (pl. tibiae)

tibial comb - comblike structure on tibia of some male odonates

trachea - air-filled tube in which gas exchange takes place in insects

type specimen - the specimen featured when a new species is described, chosen to be formally attached to that species name and represent the species in all future taxonomic studies

univoltine - with one generation per year

ventral - lower surface, underside

vertex - tiny bump on which the ocelli are located, just in front of or between the compound eyes

vesica spermalis - copulatory organ of male Anisoptera

voucher specimen - a specimen collected and preserved to confirm the presence of the species at a location and date

vulvar lamina - female subgenital plate

zygopteran - damselfly, suborder Zygoptera

Further Resources

General Interest Books

Brooks, S. *Dragonflies*. Washington: Smithsonian Books, 2003.

Cooper, A. *Dragonflies: Q&A Guide*. Mechanicsburg: Stackpole Books, 2014.

Corbet, P. S. *Dragonflies: Behavior and Ecology of Odonata*. Ithaca: Cornell University Press, 1999.

Corbet, P., & S. Brooks. *Dragonflies*. London: Collins, 2008.

Mitchell, F. L., & J. L. Lasswell. *A Dazzle of Dragonflies*. College Station: Texas A&M University Press, 2005.

Silsby, J. *Dragonflies of the World*. Washington: Smithsonian Institution Press, 2001.

van Dokkum, P. *Dragonflies: Magnificent Creatures of Water, Air, and Land*. New Haven: Yale University Press, 2015.

Field Guides

Abbott, J. C. *Damselflies of Texas. A Field Guide*. Austin: University of Texas Press, 2011.

Abbott, J. C. *Dragonflies of Texas. A Field Guide*. Austin: University of Texas Press, 2015.

Acorn, J. *Damselflies of Alberta*. Edmonton: The University of Alberta Press, 2004.

Askew, R. R. *The Dragonflies of Europe*. Colchester: Harley Books, 1988.

Bailowitz, R., D. Danforth & S. Upson. *A Field Guide to the Damselflies & Dragonflies of Arizona and Sonora*. Tucson: Nova Granada, 2015.

Beaton, G. *Dragonflies & Damselflies of Georgia and the Southeast*. Athens: University of Georgia Press, 2007.

Bedjanic, M., K. Conniff, N. van der Poorten, & A. Salamun. *Dragonfly Fauna of Sri Lanka. Distribution and Biology, with Threat Status of its Endemics*. Sofia: Pensoft, 2014.

Behrstock, R. A. *Dragonflies & Damselflies of the Southwest*. Tucson: Rio Nuevo Publishers, 2008.

Biggs, K. *Dragonflies of California and Common Dragonflies of the Southwest*. Sebastopol: Azalea Creek Publishing, 2006.

Bun, T. H., W. L. Keng, & M. Hämäläinen. *A Photographic Guide to the Dragonflies of Singapore*. Singapore: Raffles Museum of Biodiversity Reseach, 2010.

Cannings, R. A. *Introducing the Dragonflies of British Columbia and the Yukon*. Victoria: Royal British Columbia Museum, 2002.

Dijkstra, K.-D. B. *Field Guide to the Dragonflies of Britain and Europe*. Gillingham: British Wildlife Publishing, 2006.

Dijkstra, K.-D. B., & V. Clausnitzer. *The Dragonflies and Damselflies of Eastern Africa. Handbook for all Odonata from Sudan to Zimbabwe*. Studies in Afrotropical Ecology, Vol. 298. Tervuren: Royal Museum for Central Africa, 2014.

Dolny, A., D. Bárta, M. Waldhauser, O. Holusa, L. Hanel & R. Lízler. *Dragonflies of the Czech Republic*. Vlasim: Cesky svaz ochránc°¨ prírody, 2008.

DuBois, R. *Dragonflies & Damselflies of the Rocky Mountains*. Duluth: Kollath+Stensaas Publishing, 2010.

Kalkman, V., & A. Orr. *Field Guide to the Damselflies of New Guinea*. Bedum: Brachytron 16 sup., 2013.

Kerst, C., & S. Gordon. *Dragonflies and Damselflies of Oregon*. Corvallis: Oregon State University Press, 2011.

Kompier, T. *A Guide to the Dragonflies and Damselflies of the Serra dos Organos, South-eastern Brazil*. Cachoeiras de Macacu: Regua Publications, 2015.

Lam, E. *Damselflies of the Northeast*. Forest Hills: Biodiversity Books, 2004.

Manolis, T. *Dragonflies and Damselflies of California*. Berkeley, University of California Press, 2003.

May, M. L., & S. W. Dunkle. *Damselflies of North America: Color Supplement*. Gainesville: Scientific Publishers, 2007.

Meurgey, F., & L. Picard. *Les Libellules des Antilles Françaises*. Cayenne: Biotope Editions, 2011.

Michalski, J. *A Manual for the Identification of the Dragonflies and Damselflies of New Guinea, Maluku, and the Solomon Islands*. Morristown: Kanduanum Books, 2012.

Michalski, J. *The Dragonflies & Damselflies of Trinidad & Tobago*. Morristown: Kanduanum Books, 2015.

Needham, J. G., M. J. Westfall, Jr., & M. L. May. *Dragonflies of North America*. Gainesville: Scientific Publishers, 2014.

Nikula, B., J. L. Loose & M. R. Burne. *A Field Guide to the Dragonflies and Damselflies of Massachusetts*. Westborough: Massachusetts Division of Fisheries & Wildlife, 2003.

Orr, A. G. *A Guide to the Dragonflies of Borneo: Their Identification and Biology*. Kota Kinabalu: Natural History Publications (Borne), 2003.

Orr, A. G. *Dragonflies of Peninsular Malaysia and Singapore*. Kota Kinabalu: Natural History Publications (Borneo), 2005.

Orr, A., & V. Kalkman. *Field Guide to the Dragonflies of New Guinea*. Bedum: Brachytron 17 supplement, 2015.

Ozono, A., I. Kawashima, & R. Futahashi. *Dragonflies of Japan* (in Japanese). Bun-ichi Co. Ltd., 2012.

Paulson, D. *Dragonflies and Damselflies of the West*. Princeton: Princeton University Press, 2009.

Paulson, D. *Dragonflies and Damselflies of the East*. Princeton: Princeton University Press, 2011.

Polhemus, D., & A. Asquith. *Hawaiian Damselflies: A Field Identification Guide*. Honolulu: Bishop Museum Press, 1996.

Reels, G., & Zhang, H. *A Field Guide to the Dragonflies of Hainan*. Beijing: China Forestry Publishing House, 2015.

Rowe, R. *The Dragonflies of New Zealand*. Auckland: Auckland University Press, 1987.

Smallshire, D., & A. Swash. *Britain's Dragonflies. A Field Guide to the Damselflies and Dragonflies of Britain and Ireland*. Princeton: Princeton University Press, 2018.

Subramanian, K. A. *Dragonflies of India. A Field Guide*. New Delhi: Vigyan Prasar, 2009.

Suhling, F., & A. Martens. *Dragonflies and Damselflies of Namibia*. Windhoek: Gamsberg Macmillan, 2007.

Tarboton, W. & M. Tarboton. *A Guide to the Dragonflies & Damselflies of South Africa*. Cape Town: Struik Nature, 2015.

Theischinger, G., & J. Hawking. *The Complete Field Guide to Dragonflies of Australia*. Collingwood: CSIRO, 2006.

von Ellenrieder, N., & R. W. Garrison. *Dragonflies of the Yungas (Odonata). A Field Guide to the Species from Argentina*. Sofia: Pensoft, 2007.

Wang, L.-J. *Dragonflies of Taiwan*. Taiwan: 2000.

Wilson, K. D. P. *Hong Kong Dragonflies*. Hong Kong: Urban Council of Hong Kong, 1995.

Useful Websites

African Dragonflies & Damselflies Online (addo.adu.org.za)

AllOdonata (allodonata.com)

Artportalen (artportalen.se) [Sweden]

Australian Dragonflies (au.dragonflies.wildiaries.com)

Australian Dragonfly Identification Key (rnr.id.au/cgi-bin/species/odonata)

Biodiversidad Virtual (biodiversidadvirtual.org) [Spain]

Bioportal.si (bioportal.si) [Slovenia]

British Dragonfly Society (british-dragonflies.org.uk/home)

BugGuide.Net (bugguide.net/node/view/15740)

Common dragonflies in Sabah, Malaysia (wongchunxing.com/DragonFly/INDEXDragonFly.htm)

Danmarks Fugle og Natur (fugleognatur.dk) [Denmark]

Dragonflies & Damselflies of Singapore (singaporeodonata.wordpress.com)

Dragonflies & Damselflies of Thailand (thaiodonata.blogspot.com)

Dragonflies and Damselflies of Vietnam (odonatavietnam.blogspot.com)

Dragonflies of Cambodia (dragonflies-cambodia.com)

Dragonflies of Ukraine (dragonflyforall.narod.ru/index_engl.html)

Dragonfly Society of the Americas (.odonatacentral.org/index.php/PageAction.get/name/DSAHomePage)

Dragonfly World Photos (birdseye.photo/browse/location/53/world/)

Dutch Dragonflies (dutchdragonflies.eu)

iNaturalist (inaturalist.org/home)

International Odonata Research Institute (iodonata.updog.co)

Libellenwissen.de (libellenwissen.de) [Germany]

Observation.org (observation.org) [world other than Netherlands]

Odonata Central (odonatacentral.org)

Odonata of Ecuador (bdei2.cs.umb.edu/%7ewhaber/Odonata_of_Ecuador)

Odonata of India (indianodonata.org/home)

Odonata of Malaysia (odonata-of-malaysia.blogspot.my)

Odonata of Monteverde, Costa Rica (efg.cs.umb.edu/monteverde/Ode/OdeIntro.html)

Odonatologica (odonatologica.com)

Project Noah (projectnoah.org)

Slater Museum of Natural History (pugetsound.edu/academics/academic-resources/slater-museum/)

Società Italiana per lo Studio e la Conservazione delle Libellule Onlus (odonata.it) [Italy]

Ukrainian Biodiversity Information Network (izan.kiev.ua/ukrbin/index_class.php?id=714)

VietOdonata (vietodonata.blogspot.com)

Waarnemingen.be (waarnemingen.be) [Belgium]

Waarnemingen.nl (waarnemingen.nl) [The Netherlands]

World Odonata List (pugetsound.edu/academics/academic-resources/slater-museum/biodiversity-resources/dragonflies/world-odonata-list2/)

Worldwide Dragonfly Association (worlddragonfly.org)

Index

Acknowledgments

For assistance with this book, I thank K-D. Dijkstra, Matti Hämäläinen, and Ronald Orenstein for help in determining family common names and Ola Fincke, David Halstead, and Mike May for supplying dragonfly weights. K-D. Dijkstra, Ian Endersby, Benoit Guillon, Eugene Karolinsky, Cosmin Manci, Mike May, Ron Orenstein, Nancy van der Poorten, and Carlo Utzeri all provided information about websites when I asked. Kathy Biggs, Rob Cannings, Bill Carrell, K-D. Dijkstra, Sue Gregoire, George Harp, Chris Hill, Fred Lencioni, Richard Orr, and Hal White all informed me of species totals from many different locations. I greatly appreciate Scott King introducing me to dragonfly Haiku, and I thank K-D. Dijkstra and Mike May for sharing their great knowledge of Odonata by reviewing the entire manuscript.

There is not enough space to thank all the friends and colleagues who sent me photos for consideration. Fortunately, the names of all those whose images are included are listed in the credits on this page. But I must extend special thanks to Daniel Bárta, Adolfo Cordero Rivera, Marla Garrison, Benoît Guillon, Nicolas Mézière, Erland Nielsen, and Steve Valley for their enthusiasm in offering high-quality photos.

Too many people possibly to thank here have helped me over many years with encouragement, information, references, and time in the field and at meetings, often while relaxing over dinner in a Mexican restaurant. I hope all who read this will know who they are. Above all, I thank my wife, Netta Smith, for all her years of love and patience while we planned our life in part around dragonflies. She also turned out to be a superb photographer of these insects.

The publisher would like to thank the following for permission to reproduce copyright material:

John Abbott 1tr, 168. Alamy Stock Photo/ Sabena Jane Blackbird 99b, blickwinkel 92, Ger Bosma 51t, Danita Delimont 191b, Robert Henno 128t, Imagems 167t, Suzanne Long 16b, Gerry Pearce 52, Morley Read 20r, Ian Redding 57, Sue Robinson 173, Paul Sparks 191t, komkrit tonusin 51 b, Wong Hock weng 17. Dan Bárta front cover, 85t, 107, 198, 206tl. Marcus Beard 5. Gif Beaton 131m. Robert A Behrstock 39t. Dave Biggs 175t. Steve Bird 197b. Thomas Coombs-Hahn 169t. Adolfo Cordero Rivera 27 both, 147 both, 205tr, 209tl. Carel de Haseth 1tm, 96. Jürg De Marmels 206bl. Marion Dobbs 59, 105 both. Larry Engles 53 all. Ted Eubanks 207bl. FLPA/ Paul Hobson 22, Imagebroker/Marko Kanig 21, Minden Pictures/Ernst Dirksen, Buiten-beeld 60b, Minden Pictures/ Michael Durham 50b, Minden Pictures/Steve Gettle 171, Minden Pictures/Rene Krekels, NiS 103. Marla Garrison 4, 133l. Rosser Garrison 208tr. Getty Images/ Joe Petersburger 48. Maciej Górka 212tl.Christian Goyaud 211tr. Benoît Guillon 35 both, 97, 102m, 109 both, 126, 143b, 167b, 204br, 208bl, 217. William A. Haber 69br, 204tr. Jan Hamrsky 130 all, 131b. Naoya Ishizawa 47, 113. Jim Johnson 207br. Vincent Kalkman 140b, 208br. Steve Krotzer 129. Jeff Larson 153. Greg Lasley back cover, 161. Tony Leukering 141t. Dan Logen 61 l. Pablo Martinez-Darve Sanz 31t, 37 both, 151, 193 both, 205bl. Nicolas Mézière 31b, 201, 205tl, 206br, 213br. Marceau Minot 207tr. Nature Picture Library/ Nature Production 211tl, Cyril Ruoso 16t, Lynn M Stone 8, Nick Upton 90b, Doug Wechsler 159b, Bert Willaert 24. Bergman Ng 185. Erland Nielsen 1tl, bl & br, 3, 7, 18 both, 19r, 29, 33, 58r, 64, 65, 75 both, 85b, 88, 91, 111 both, 125, 135, 143t, 183, 187 both, 204bl, 205br, 207tl, 209tr, 210tr & bl, 211bl & br, 214tr. OdonataCentral.org 170b. Dennis Paulson 19l, 11t, 12 both, 13, 14tl, 15, 19l, 20t, 23 both, 25 both, 39b, 41 all, 45 both, 55b, 56 both, 62 both, 63, 67 both, 69t & bl, 71t, 73t & m, 77 all, 81bl & br, 83bl & br, 93, 94, 95, 98, 99tl & tr, 100 both, 101 both, 102t, 117b, 121, 128b, 133r, 137 both, 139, 140t, 149 both, 155, 157 both, 163t, 164, 166t, 169b, 170t, 172b, 177, 179 both, 189 both, 195 both, 202, 210tl & br, 212br, 213bl. Fons Peels 117t. Nicholas Pollock 181. Reiner Richter 119, 204tl. Shutterstock/gp.riccardi 166b, Greg Brave 172t. Dave Smallshire 203. Netta Smith 11b, 43, 71b, 73b, 81t, 83t, 90t, 115, 123 both, 136 all, 141b, 145 both, 159t, 163b, 174 both, 175b, 197t, 200 both, 208tl, 209bl & br. Buck Snelson 58l. Dirk Stevenson 61r. Leonard Tan 213tl. Warwick Tarboton 79. Tim Termaat 206tr. Gregg Thompson 60t, 87. Steve Valley 10, 14r, 55t, 132. Johan van't Bosch 212tr. Keith Wilson 212bl.

All reasonable efforts have been made to trace copyright holders and to obtain their permission for the use of copyright material. The publisher apologizes for any errors or omissions and will gratefully incorporate any corrections in future reprints if notified.